INDIAN

POCAHONT...
SACAGAWE...
SITTING B... *Stevenson*
TECUMSEH, *Stevenson*

NAVAL HEROES

DAVID FARRAGUT, *Long*
GEORGE DEWEY, *Long*
JOHN PAUL JONES, *Snow*
MATTHEW CALBRAITH PERRY, *Schambach*
OLIVER HAZARD PERRY, *Long*
RAPHAEL SEMMES, *Snow*
STEPHEN DECATUR, *Smith*

NOTED WIVES and MOTHERS

ABIGAIL ADAMS, *Wagoner*
DOLLY MADISON, *Monsell*
JESSIE FREMONT, *Wagoner*
MARTHA WASHINGTON, *Wagoner*
MARY TODD LINCOLN, *Wilkie*
NANCY HANKS, *Stevenson*
RACHEL JACKSON, *Govan*

SCIENTISTS and INVENTORS

ALECK BELL, *Widdemer*
ELI WHITNEY, *Snow*
GEORGE CARVER, *Stevenson*
GEORGE EASTMAN, *Henry*
HENRY FORD, *Aird-Ruddiman*
JOHN AUDUBON, *Mason*
LUTHER BURBANK, *Burt*
MARIA MITCHELL, *Melin*
ROBERT FULTON, *Henry*
SAMUEL MORSE, *Snow*
TOM EDISON, *Guthridge*
WALTER REED, *Higgins*
WILBUR AND ORVILLE WRIGHT, *Stevenson*
WILL AND CHARLIE MAYO, *Hammontree*

CIVIC LEADERS

BETSY ROSS, *Weil*
BOOKER T. WASHINGTON, *Stevenson*
CLARA BARTON, *Stevenson*
DAN BEARD, *Mason*
JANE ADDAMS, *Wagoner*
JULIA WARD HOWE, *Wagoner*
JULIETTE LOW, *Higgins*
LUCRETIA MOTT, *Burnett*
MOLLY PITCHER, *Stevenson*
SUSAN ANTHONY, *Monsell*

SOLDIERS

ANTHONY WAYNE, *Stevenson*
BEDFORD FORREST, *Parks*
DAN MORGAN, *Bryant*
ETHAN ALLAN, *Winders*
FRANCIS MARION, *Steele*
ISRAEL PUTNAM, *Stevenson*
JEB STUART, *Winders*
NATHANAEL GREENE, *Peckham*
ROBERT E. LEE, *Monsell*
TOM JACKSON, *Monsell*
U. S. GRANT, *Stevenson*
WILLIAM HENRY HARRISON, *Peckham*
ZACK TAYLOR, *Wilkie*

STATESMEN

ABE LINCOLN, *Stevenson*
ANDY JACKSON, *Stevenson*
DAN WEBSTER, *Smith*
FRANKLIN ROOSEVELT, *Weil*
HENRY CLAY, *Monsell*
JAMES MONROE, *Widdemer*
JOHN MARSHALL, *Monsell*
SAM HOUSTON, *Stevenson*
TEDDY ROOSEVELT, *Parks*
WOODROW WILSON, *Monsell*

Jeff Davis

Confederate Boy

Illustrated by Robert Doremus

Jeff Davis

Confederate Boy

*By Lena Young de Grummond
and
Lynn de Grummond Delaune*

THE **BOBBS-MERRILL** COMPANY, INC.
A SUBSIDIARY OF HOWARD W. SAMS & CO., INC.
Publishers · INDIANAPOLIS · NEW YORK

To Richie and Linden, descendants of Jefferson Davis' sister, Anna Davis Smith

The authors wish to express their appreciation to Mr. Hudson Strode, whose books have helped to restore Jefferson Davis, President of the Confederacy, to his rightful place as a famous American

Illustrations

Full pages

Numerous smaller illustrations

Contents

CHILDHOOD
OF FAMOUS
AMERICANS

★   ★   ★

★ ★ Jeff Davis

Confederate Boy

Barefoot Time

THE SPRING of 1813 was a cool one. Jeff had heard his father say he didn't remember another winter this long since they'd moved to Mississippi.

"But it's getting warmer now," said Jeff to himself. "I surely ought to be able to find some today!"

Jeff jumped off the high back porch of the Big House. Everyone on Rosemont Plantation called the Davis home the "Big House." It was much bigger than the many small houses on Rosemont where the servants and field hands lived. It was the center of life on the plantation, too.

Sitting on the ground behind the house was a

little Negro boy. "Good morning, James Pemberton," said Jeff. "What are you doing?"

The little Negro boy looked up. "I'm learning how to whittle," he said. He was bending over a small piece of wood. In one hand he had a knife. He was shaving slivers off a piece of wood.

Jeff sat down beside him. The two boys were almost exactly the same age. They had been companions and playmates all their lives. Jeff was five, the only member of his big family who was too young to go to school. He'd have been very lonely without James Pemberton.

"That'll make a good boat, Jim," said Jeff. "If we ever get to go wading, that is. You haven't seen any yet, have you?"

Jim knew what Jeff was talking about at once.

"No, I haven't, Mister Jeff, not anywhere," he said. "I looked behind Aunt Serena's cabin last night before I went to bed. There aren't any down there yet, though."

"I'm on my way to look now," said Jeff. He stood up. "How about trying the cottonwoods this morning? We haven't looked there for about a week."

"All right," said Jim. He carefully closed his knife. He put it and the piece of wood in his pocket as he stood up.

"I hope we find some soon," said Jeff. "I'm getting mighty tired of waiting."

The two boys walked across the big back yard, past the stables, and into the woods beyond. After a few minutes they stopped near a clump of graceful trees.

"No, there aren't any here yet," said Jeff, looking up at the branches. "We'll try above the gully next. If there aren't any there, we'll just have to give up on the cottonwoods."

The two boys walked on through the woods. Soon they came to a little hill. On the other side was a gully or ditch almost as deep as Jeff was tall—and Jeff was tall for his age. He was already as big as his sister Pollie, who was two years older.

"I think I see something, Jim!" cried Jeff excitedly. "Look up at the top of that tallest tree."

The two boys ran to the clump of trees nearest the gully. Eagerly they searched the branches.

"I don't see anything, Mister Jeff," said Jim.

"No, neither do I," said Jeff with a sigh. "It must have been the way the sun was shining on the branches." He sat down at the foot of the trees.

"I don't know if we're ever going to find any this year," said Jim, sitting down beside him.

"Well," said Jeff, after a few minutes, "we can swing anyway." He stood up.

Jeff grabbed a heavy vine which hung from the largest tree on the hill. He pulled it back as far from the tree as it would go. Then, running as fast as he could, he raced toward the edge of

the gully. He was going so fast that he and the
vine flew all the way across the wide gully.

When Jeff reached the other side, he put his
feet down as soon as he could touch the ground.
Still holding onto the vine, he ran until he could
stop.

"Are you ready, Jim?" he called across the
gully.

"I'm ready," Jim called back.

The Negro boy stood up and waited. Jeff

15

swung the vine back across the gully to him. Jim caught it. In a few minutes he, too, was flying across the gully. He landed near Jeff and handed him the thick vine rope.

"Here I go!" cried Jeff. Off he went in a running start, as he had done before. Then he went sailing back across the gully. He and Jim swung back and forth many times.

Suddenly Jeff stopped. He was standing with the vine in his hand, ready to swing. "Listen," he said. He and Jim stood perfectly still. *Bong, bong! Bong, bong!*

"The dinner bell," said Jim.

"I thought I'd heard it," said Jeff. The two boys turned and ran through the woods. The big plantation bell which was used to call the family to the Big House for dinner kept ringing.

"I'll race you to the back steps!" called Jeff. Off they ran. They were neck and neck when they threw themselves on the back steps, panting.

16

"I'd say that race was a tie."

The boys looked up. Jeff's oldest sister Anna was standing on the long back porch.

"Better hurry, James. Serena's looking for you. I was waiting for you, too, Jeff. I thought maybe you hadn't heard the bell. I was going to ask Sam to ring it a few more times just for you."

"We were down in the cottonwoods, swinging across the gully," said Jeff, as he climbed the steps.

Anna brushed some leaves and dirt from his trousers. "I guessed that maybe you had been doing something of the sort," she said, smiling. "I told Mamma I'd help you wash up."

The two went into the house. Anna was like a second mother to Jeff. When he was born, his mother had been very sick. She had been too sick to take care of him. Anna was his oldest sister. His crib had been put in her room. She had taken care of him from the beginning.

"There," said Anna, as she helped Jeff part his hair. "Now you'll pass inspection."

Jeff was already at the door. "Let's hurry," he said. "I'm hungry. I can smell Serena's biscuits from here."

Anna laughed. "All right," she said. "I think we're last anyway."

They were last. When they went into the dining room, the others were already sitting at the huge table. It had to be a big table, too, because the Davises were a big family. Jeff had nine brothers and sisters!

"Well, here you are!" Mr. Davis said to Jeff. "I thought maybe Anna had to have Sam pull you out of the top of the tallest dogwood tree somewhere! Have you found what you're looking for yet?"

All the people at the table smiled. They knew about Jeff's hunt.

"No, sir," said Jeff, sitting at his place at the

table. He took a big white napkin from the small silver ring with "Jefferson" engraved on it. "I'm still looking, though."

"Remind me to tell you something after dinner," said Isaac. He was the only other Davis son at home. Joseph, Benjamin, and Samuel, Jr., Jeff's three oldest brothers, had gone off to fight the British in the War of 1812.

Isaac was a member of the Mississippi Home Guard, like most of the other older boys in Wilkinson County. He was ready to fight if he was needed, but he could still stay home and help his father run the plantation.

Isaac sat next to the vacant chairs of the older brothers. Next came Jeff's father, Mr. Samuel Davis. Pollie, the sister just older than Jeff, sat on the other side of Mr. Davis. Then came the four older sisters. Their names went together so well that Jeff had made a little song of them. All strung together they sounded like a poem.

"Anna, Lucinda,
Amanda, Mathilda."

At the end of the table opposite Mr. Davis sat Jeff's mother, Jane. Next to her, on the side of the table with the other boys, sat Jeff.

"I thought I smelled biscuits," said Jeff. He helped himself from the plate that Serena, the Negro cook, placed on the table.

"I'm surprised you didn't smell them from out in the cottonwoods," said his mother with a smile. "You like them so much."

"I hope this cool spell is over," said Mr. Davis. "The cotton and tobacco won't grow well if we don't start having warm weather pretty soon."

"Yes, sir," agreed Isaac. "It's definitely warmer today, though."

"Yes, it is," said Mr. Davis. "I even found it hot when I was in the kitchen this morning. I almost thought we'd need the punkah."

Jeff looked up at the ceiling. The big wooden

fan-shaped punkah was still. When the warm weather arrived, the punkah would be used at every meal.

A little Negro boy would sit on the floor near a far wall. He would pull the rope that went up the wall, across the ceiling, and over to the punkah above the table. The rope would pull the punkah slowly back and forth like a giant fan. It would keep flies away from the table. It would make a breeze to keep the family cool.

Mr. Davis and Isaac talked about plantation business. Jeff didn't pay much attention to their talk at first. He was still wondering where he should look next on his hunt. His ears pricked up, however, when he heard Mr. Davis talking about horses. The plantation was famous for its fine horses.

"Everybody knows Papa raises the best horses in the whole South!" thought Jeff proudly.

Horses were very much on Jeff's mind these

days. Isaac was teaching him to ride. Mr. Davis was thinking about those lessons, too, for he said, "How's Jeff coming with his riding, Isaac?"

"Well, he's had only a couple of lessons so far, sir, but I think he's coming along pretty well. It shouldn't be too long before he's ready for that pony you promised him." Isaac smiled at Jeff.

"Do you think I could have him this summer, Papa?" Jeff asked eagerly. "I could practice riding all summer. Then maybe I'd be able to ride pretty well by the time school starts."

Mr. Davis smiled. "We'll see, son," he said, and went on eating.

Jeff had just finished a big piece of chocolate cake. He was putting his napkin back into its silver ring when Isaac stopped by his chair.

"Go look at the clump of trees on the south field road," the older boy said. "I thought I saw some when we rode in to dinner today."

"You did?" asked Jeff, jumping up.

He was already out of the dining room when Isaac called, "You can ride out with me if you want to."

"Are you going right now?" asked Jeff, stopping in his tracks. "You don't have to wait for Papa?"

"No," said Isaac, "I'll take you right now."

A few minutes later, the two boys were on their way. Isaac rode in the saddle. Jeff sat behind and put his arms around Isaac.

Isaac stopped his horse near a clump of trees. "There," he said. "I thought I'd seen some."

"Hooray!" yelled Jeff, slipping to the ground. In a few minutes he had climbed up into one of the trees. He broke off a branch of lovely white flowers and jumped to the ground.

Now he turned to run down the road back to the Big House. Just then Mr. Davis came into view. He was riding his big black horse Jupiter toward the field.

"Papa! Papa!" cried Jeff, excitedly waving the branch. "The dogwood's in bloom—now may I go barefooted?"

Mr. Davis stopped Jupiter right where he was. He threw back his head and laughed. Then he was more serious. "You've certainly hunted for it a long time. I hope you'll stick to more serious projects as well," he said. Then he smiled again.

"Your mother and I have always said our children could start going barefooted when the first dogwood blooms, so you may."

Jeff sat down right in the dusty road. Off came shoes. Off came stockings. "May I go wading in the creek, too, Papa?" Jeff asked eagerly.

"Yes," said Mr. Davis, still smiling. Jeff started off. "Only don't leave your shoes and stockings here," Papa added.

"No, sir," said Jeff. He had been in such a hurry to start, he hadn't even thought about his

clothes. In another second he was running down the dusty road, shoes and stockings in hand.

Jeff and James Pemberton spent the afternoon wading in the creek. It seemed to them they'd been there only a few minutes—instead of a few hours—when they heard the big bell ring for supper.

As Jeff was getting ready for bed that night, he said to Anna, "Why does everything always take so long, Anna?"

"What do you mean?" she asked.

"Well, I had to wait and wait and wait before I could find the dogwood blossoms. I hunted for them for ages. Now I have to wait and wait and wait to get my pony. Papa didn't sound as though he were even thinking about my getting it soon," said Jeff.

Anna put her hand on his shoulder. "You finally found the dogwood blossoms, though. Now that warm weather's coming, the days will go by fast. You'll probably be ready for that pony before you know it." She smiled and kissed him good night.

"I surely hope so," said Jeff, snuggling down in his bed. It had been a good day. He had found the dogwood blossoms. He had gone barefooted and all—but, oh, how much better every day would be when he got a pony of his very own!

Riptide of Rosemont

"MISTER JEFF, Mister Jeff!" Jeff turned over in bed and opened his eyes slowly. Bending over him was James Pemberton.

Jeff knew Jim so well that he could tell just by looking at him that Jim knew something exciting. His eyes were shining. His grin was even wider than usual.

"What is it, Jim? What's happened?" asked Jeff. "You look just as you do on Christmas Eve when you've been helping to hide the presents. What's happened?"

Jeff already was tumbling out of bed. Even as he spoke, he began to pull on his clothes. If something exciting was going to happen, he certainly didn't want to miss a minute of it.

Jim grinned again. "Why nothing's happened, Mister Jeff. I just brought you some hot water to wash with. You'll have to hurry if you don't want to be late for breakfast."

Jim poured steaming hot water from a big copper kettle into a white china pitcher on Jeff's night stand.

"When I took Mister Isaac his hot water, he said I should make sure you didn't oversleep *this* morning."

Still grinning, Jim went out the bedroom door. Jeff could hear him whistling as he went downstairs to take the kettle back to the kitchen.

"I wonder what's so special about *this* morning," said Jeff to himself. He gave himself the kind of washing his mother called "a lick and a promise." In another second, he was racing down the steps, two at a time.

"Whoa, there! You won't be able to stop till you hit the front lane at that rate, young man!" Mr. Davis was standing in the big front hall near the dining room door.

"Papa!" cried Jeff. "I didn't even know you were back!" He rushed to his father and threw both arms around him, as Mr. Davis leaned down to give him a big hug.

"I got home late last night," said Mr. Davis. "I finished my business in Natchez a little sooner than I thought I would, so I came on home." He smiled and mussed Jeff's hair a little. "You don't mind my coming back a few days early, do you?"

"No, sir!" said Jeff, laughing.

Mr. Davis laughed, too. When he and Jeff walked into the dining room, the rest of the family were already there, waiting for them.

As Jeff kissed his mother and Anna good morning, it seemed to him they had a special sort of smile for him. In fact, all through breakfast, Jeff thought the whole family kept looking at him and smiling.

"Just like Jim—they all look as though they know something extra nice," Jeff thought. "Of course, having Papa home again is something extra nice," he added to himself. Just the same, he could feel a tiny ball of excitement growing little by little inside him.

Jeff enjoyed hearing all about his brother Joseph in Natchez. He enjoyed hearing the latest news from the city, too, but he was glad when Papa rolled up his napkin and put it into the heavy silver napkin ring with "Samuel" engraved on it. When Papa pushed his chair back from the table, Jeff jumped up, too.

The whole family stood up.

Usually Mamma went to the kitchen to plan things with Serena. Anna and the other girls went to the sitting room to sew. Isaac and Papa went to the stables before going to the fields.

This morning everybody went in one direction. They all moved down the front hall toward the porch.

"The family acts just as though we were going to meet company," thought Jeff. He was sure now that something unusual was going to happen.

Suddenly Mr. Davis stopped. "Jeff," he said, "I've left my spectacles on the sideboard. Please run back to the dining room and get them for me."

Jeff looked up. He almost wanted to ask if something so unexciting as spectacles couldn't wait, but his papa said, "Hurry, Jeff."

"Yes, sir," the boy said, bounding off at top speed. He was anxious to get back to find out what was happening.

A few seconds later, Jeff came running down the hall. Everyone else was already outside, so he rushed through the front door. The whole family stood on the porch, looking at him. And there, beyond the porch, just at the bottom of the front steps was——

"My horse!" cried Jeff. He was off the high porch and on the ground in one great leap. "My horse! Oh, Papa, you brought my horse from Natchez!" Jeff was already rubbing the shiny dark nose and stroking the chestnut mane. "Oh, Papa, thank you!"

In one second, he had leaped up the porch steps, hugged his smiling father, and then leaped

back down beside his horse. "May I ride him now, Papa? May I?"

"For goodness' sake, Papa, hurry and say 'yes,'" laughed Anna. "I don't think Jeff will be able to stand it another minute if you don't."

Mr. Davis nodded. "You may ride, Jeff—that is, as soon as I have my spectacles safe and sound again."

Jeff looked down at the eyeglasses in his hand. He'd forgotten them completely! He hurried back up the steps and gave the spectacles to his father.

"I think Jeff's forgotten we have steps," said Mamma, as Jeff leaped off the porch once more to mount his horse.

James Pemberton, who had been holding the bridle, gave it to Jeff as the little horseman climbed into the new saddle. He was all ready to say "Giddap" when he suddenly stopped.

"What's his name, Papa?" Jeff asked.

"Riptide—Riptide of Rosemont, Jeff," answered Mr. Davis.

"Giddap, Rip!" said Jeff. Off he galloped down the lane. "Oh, Rip," Jeff said as they rode past the rose bushes that gave Rosemont Plantation its name, "you're the most wonderful horse in the world!"

"We Will
Not Run"

IT SEEMED to Jeff that the summer flew by. Every day he and James Pemberton spent hours with Rip. Right after he got his pony, Jeff had said, "We'll have to brush Rip every day, Jim. Papa gave me two currycombs for us to use. I don't know how much brushing it'll take to keep him pretty, but I guess it'll be a good bit.

"Once I heard Anna tell Pollie she should brush her hair one hundred strokes every night to make it shiny. I guess we'll have to brush Rip's hair a hundred strokes, too."

The boys didn't mind brushing Rip. They loved taking care of him as well as riding him.

One August morning Mrs. Davis was making a cake in the kitchen. She saw Jeff and Jim go riding by the kitchen window. "Jeff has almost lived on that horse this summer," she said.

Anna was sifting flour for the cake while her mother creamed the butter and sugar. "I think he only gets off to eat and sleep," she said.

"He'd really like to eat and sleep on Rip, too," said Mamma, smiling.

"I'm afraid he'll miss Rip during his first days of school," said Anna thoughtfully.

"He probably will," said Mrs. Davis, "but I'm sure he'll like school, too. It won't take him long to get used to being away from Rip part of the time." She stopped beating the butter-and-sugar mixture. "Would you please hand me the eggs."

"Yes, ma'am," said Anna, moving over to the egg basket. She was still thinking of Jeff's starting to school, though. She was still a little worried.

Anna needn't have worried. Jeff enjoyed school. "I miss Rip," he said, when she asked him, "but there's always something interesting to do at school. Besides I get to ride Rip when I'm home. Maybe later on Papa will let me ride him to school, too."

"I'm not sure about that," said Anna, "because we need you to walk through the woods with Pollie. We count on you to look after her, you know."

"Well, I'll try," replied Jeff. "Mamma told me that I was the 'man' and that I should look out for her."

"That's right," said Anna. "Even though she's older than you are, you're already bigger than she is. I saw you carrying the lunch basket the other day. That's very nice."

"It's pretty heavy sometimes," said Jeff. "Serena surely puts good things in it." He turned to Anna. "What kind of cake are you and

Mamma going to make tomorrow? I liked that chocolate one you made last week."

"Well, you might find more chocolate cake in your lunch one of these days," Anna said with a wink. "Now if you hurry and change your clothes, you might have time to ride Rip before supper."

Jeff scampered away, taking off his jacket as he ran.

Early the next morning, Jeff and his sister Pollie started to walk to the Old Field School. The school was in a log cabin, a mile from Rosemont Plantation.

"There are certainly lots of birds singing this morning," said Pollie, looking up at the branches overhead. "They must think it's going to be a very nice day."

"Maybe they know we have chocolate cake in our lunch," said Jeff with a grin.

"How do you know?" laughed Pollie.

"I asked Serena," said Jeff, giving the lunch basket a little swing. Then he said, "Listen! There must be a thousand cardinals in the woods this morning."

This morning was like any other morning, except that maybe it was a little warmer and sunnier, and more birds were singing. When Jeff and Pollie got to school, though, they found something different.

The children were talking in a little group.

Even at a distance, Jeff could tell they were excited. Then one of the boys in the group saw the Davis children coming.

"Jeff! Jeff!" Jeff's friend, Tom Sanders, came running up to him. "Have you heard about Mr. Squally? He's here!"

"Mr. Squally?" asked Jeff. "Who is he?"

"Don't you know?" asked Tom. "He's the chair-mender who travels from town to town carrying chairs upside down on his head. Right now he's working here around Woodville. Everyone is talking about him."

And everybody was. The children were gathered in a little knot outside the schoolhouse door. All of them were talking at once.

"What's so strange about a chair-mender anyway?" asked Jeff. He couldn't understand all of this excitement.

"Haven't you ever seen him?" asked another boy. "He is the ugliest, meanest-looking man I have ever seen. He has a great big scar on one cheek, and he wears a patch over one eye. Oh! He's terrible looking!"

"You shouldn't judge a person by his looks," said Jeff. "Mr. Squally may be very nice. Have you ever talked with him, Tom?"

"No!" exclaimed Tom, "and if I ever see him coming, I'll run away."

"I will, too!" shouted another child.

Just then Mr. Winters rang the bell. The children lined up for school. Even though school went as usual, Jeff could feel everyone's excitement. At recess, the children were still talking about Mr. Squally.

After school was dismissed, Jeff and Pollie started home. The familiar path through the woods seemed different this afternoon.

"It surely is cloudy," said Jeff, looking at the dark sky.

"Yes," said Pollie, shivering a little. "It isn't

at all sunny and pretty as it was this morning when we came."

"No," replied Jeff. "I wonder where all the squirrels are this afternoon. I haven't seen a one." Usually he and Pollie saw many squirrels frisk across their path and scoot up the tall trees. They enjoyed watching squirrels.

"There aren't any birds singing, either," added Pollie.

The two children didn't say much as they walked deeper into the woods. There seemed to be moving shadows and rustling noises every-where.

Suddenly Pollie stopped. She grabbed Jeff's arm. "I hear somebody coming!" she said.

Jeff and Pollie stood still, listening, but for a moment everything was quiet. Then, suddenly, they saw the dim outline of a figure, moving through the woods.

They couldn't make out what the figure was,

but they could tell that it had tall pointed things wobbling on its head! And it was coming directly toward them!

"Oh, Jeff!" cried Pollie in a terrified whisper. "It's Mr. Squally! I can see the chairs on top of his head." She pulled on Jeff's coat and started to back down the path.

Jeff's heart was beating fast. He was trembling, but he took hold of Pollie's hand. Then he planted himself firmly in the path. Speaking as steadily as he could, he said, "We will not run."

Suddenly the figure burst out of the underbrush near them. It was not Mr. Squally! It was a big deer with long antlers.

The deer came close to the two children. It stood still for a minute and looked at them with great brown eyes. It was so close that Jeff could feel its warm breath. Then, slowly, the animal walked back into the woods.

"Whew!" said Jeff, letting out a long sigh.

44

"Oh, let's go home, Jeff!" said Pollie. She was about to cry.

"All right," agreed Jeff. He didn't want anyone to know it, but he'd be glad to get home, too. "Let's go!"

Jeff and Pollie ran hand in hand as fast as they could. They didn't stop running until they could see the rose hedges around their house at Rosemont.

That evening at supper Pollie told the family

what had happened in the woods. When she had finished, Mrs. Davis spoke.

"I'm proud of the way you acted, Jeff," she said, putting her hand on her son's shoulder.

"Well," said Jeff, "I must admit I was glad we didn't meet Mr. Squally. The deer was so big, though, and came so close that I was glad when it left—as glad as I would have been if it had been Mr. Squally."

Company
Coming

THE DAYS passed more quickly than Jeff would have believed possible. In no time at all the school year was over. Vacation time had come.

"I'll miss school and Tom and everybody," thought Jeff, "but I'll be able to ride Rip all day now! I can't think of anything nicer than that."

One morning after breakfast, Jeff walked toward the stables. The sun shone down lazily. The whole world seemed warm and sunny and happy. Jeff put his hands in his pockets and whistled. He scuffed up the dust with his feet.

As he neared the stables, he saw Sam, one of the colored men who took care of the horses.

Sam was leading two of Mr. Davis's big gray horses out of their stalls.

"Sam!" called Jeff, running forward. "Where are you taking those horses? Papa and Isaac aren't going anywhere, are they?"

"Good morning, Mister Jeff," said Sam. "Whoa, there, boys! Whoa!" He pulled the two big gray horses to a halt.

Sam turned to Jeff, "No, sir, your papa and Mister Isaac aren't going anywhere. It's just that we have some other horses coming. Your papa said to move some of the horses in the east stables around to the stalls in the back. He wants the five stalls nearest the house to be empty."

"I wonder if we're getting some new horses from Natchez," Jeff said. "I haven't heard Papa say anything about it, though. Have you, Sam?"

"No, Mister Jeff, I haven't. It might be that some visitors are coming, and your papa wants a place to keep their horses," suggested Sam.

"Oh!" exclaimed Jeff, his eyes shining. "Maybe that's it, but I haven't heard anything about it before."

Having company come was always an important event. Usually everybody on the plantation knew about it before the great day actually arrived.

When company was expected, there were all sorts of extra preparations. Special cakes were baked. The best china was brought out. James Pemberton's sister, Mar'sue, helped polish the big silver platters and bowls. There was much activity all through the big plantation house. Sometimes, though, nobody knew about company until just before they arrived.

Jeff was just starting to follow Sam when he heard his name.

"Jeff! Jeff! Come here, Jeff!" It was Anna calling him. She was hurrying down from the Big House toward the stables.

"Here I am, Anna!" Jeff called. He ran to meet her.

"I was sure I'd find you down here," she said. "I believe you and James Pemberton spend as much time at the stables as Rip does."

Jeff grinned. "I guess we do," he said. "Papa will have to make a stall for us, too." Then he remembered what Sam had said.

"Anna, Sam's moving horses from the front stalls to the back stalls. He says we aren't getting any new horses, so he thinks maybe there might be some company coming."

"He's right," said Anna. "There is company coming. Papa just got word about a half-hour ago that some friends of Joseph's are coming."

"Is Joseph coming, too?" asked Jeff eagerly. He always loved Joseph's visits from Natchez. His oldest brother always had so many interesting things to talk about—his horses, his plantation at Natchez, his trips, people he knew.

50

"No," said Anna. "Joseph can't leave Natchez right now, but maybe he'll come later. The person who's coming is someone Joseph knew during the war. His name is Major Hinds. He'll have his family with him, but we don't know exactly how many there'll be. The Major and his family are going to visit for a while before they leave for Kentucky."

Jeff stopped short. "Kentucky!" he exclaimed. "Why, Kentucky's a million miles from here! There are Indians everywhere, too! The Major's family probably will all be killed."

Anna laughed. "My goodness, Jeff," she said, "you know they don't have to be afraid of Indians. All the Indians in northern Mississippi are friendly. They're mostly Choctaws, and they fought on our side during the war."

"Just the same, nobody can tell what might happen on the way to Kentucky! It really is a million miles away, isn't it?" Jeff asked.

"It seems that far, Jeff," replied Anna, "but it isn't really. I've heard Papa say it's about seven hundred miles. That's a long trip, though, and it will take the Major's family weeks and weeks to get there."

By this time Anna and Jeff had reached the back steps. Already the Big House was busier than usual. Little Missy, with her pigtails bobbing, flew past them down the steps. She had a big egg basket in her hand.

"Serena must be getting ready to start on the

cakes," said Anna. "I think I'll go to the kitchen to see what Mamma wants me to help with now."

"Oh," she said, turning to Jeff, "I almost forgot. Mamma sent me to tell you to put on clean clothes. Then you're to stay close to the house. Mamma wants you to be near by—and clean—when the company comes."

"Yes, ma'am," said Jeff. He went up the stairs almost without knowing what he was doing. His head was full of Indians, horseback rides through dark forests, and all the other adventures that surely would be part of a trip to Kentucky.

After dinner Jeff rushed out to the kitchen. James Pemberton was sitting on a high stool, happily licking cake icing from a big wooden spoon.

"Jim," Jeff said, "let's go out and watch for the company."

"All right," said Jim, hopping down.

"James Pemberton, don't you take that spoon

outside. That's my best cake-mixing spoon," said Serena.

"Yes, ma'am," said Jim, giving the spoon one last lick before handing it to her.

The two boys walked out to the biggest live oak tree near the road. It stood on a little hill. From the hill, the boys could see the visitors as soon as they rounded the bend in the road. The huge roots of the big tree offered many nice seats for the boys to choose, too.

"We might as well have a game of 'Old Horse' while we wait," said Jeff.

Jim agreed, so both boys started to gather acorns from around the big tree.

"Now," said Jeff, a few minutes later, "are you ready?"

"I'm ready," said Jim.

Jeff turned his back to the other boy. From a pile of acorns he had hidden in the roots of the tree, he picked up five acorns. Then he turned back to Jim, holding out both his closed fists.

"Old Horse," he said. "Who'll ride him?"

"I will," said Jim.

"How many miles?" asked Jeff.

"Four," said Jim, looking at Jeff's closed fists.

"Wrong!" said Jeff triumphantly. "Give me four!"

Jim counted out four acorns from his pile and gave them to Jeff. Now it was Jeff's turn to guess. If he were right, he would get all the acorns Jim had in his hands. If he were wrong, he would have to give Jim the number he had guessed. It was almost suppertime when the boys decided to stop to count their acorns. The one who had the most won the game.

"Twelve, thirteen, fourteen," Jeff counted. He was just starting to count the acorns in one of his other piles when he saw a little cloud of dust far down at the bend of the road.

"Look, Jim!" he cried, jumping to his feet. Acorns spilled in all directions. "The company must be coming!"

James Pemberton leaped to his feet, too. Both boys stood still for a minute, taking one long look as the group of riders came into sight.

"Come on, Jim!" shouted Jeff. He turned and raced toward the Big House with Jim at his heels. Up the road and across the long, long yard the two boys dashed at full speed.

Mr. Davis and Isaac already had come in from the fields. They were sitting in rockers on the long porch.

"Papa! Papa!" called Jeff, bounding up the front steps two at a time. "They're here! Major Hinds and his folks are here! Jim and I saw them coming around the bend where the rose hedge starts."

"Well, that's fine," said Mr. Davis. "Go inside and tell your mother. James, you go to the

56

kitchen and tell Serena that she can start supper now. She's been waiting. Come on, Isaac, we'll walk down to meet our company. I'm glad they arrived before dark."

In a short time, there was much bustle and hurry as Major Hinds and his party were welcomed. Jeff stood on the porch with the rest of the family to greet them as they rode up. Mr. Davis and Isaac were with the guest. Sam and two stable boys helped the visitors down from their horses.

"How nice to meet you and your family, Major Hinds," said Mrs. Davis, coming forward to greet the guests. "We were so pleased when Joseph sent word that you would be coming to see us."

"We're pleased to be here, ma'am," said Major Hinds, taking off his hat. He was a tall, strong-looking man, handsome in his uniform.

The Major turned to introduce the other members of his party. "This is my wife, Mary," he said. A small, pretty woman with wavy brown hair moved up to meet Mrs. Davis.

"This is my wife's sister Beulah." The other woman in the group stepped forward. "This young lady is my niece Elizabeth," he said, introducing a girl about fifteen years old.

Then Major Hinds introduced the person who had interested Jeff the most. "This is my son, Howell. He's seven years old."

Major Hinds looked at Jeff and smiled. "Unless I'm mistaken," he said, "this handsome young fellow must be the Jeff we've heard so much about from Joseph. I believe you're just about Howie's age."

"Yes, sir," said Jeff, "I just had a birthday last month."

"Son," said Mr. Davis to Jeff, "suppose you show Howell where he can wash up and then you may eat supper."

When company came, the children ate supper first. They ate by themselves. The grownups ate later.

"Howell will sleep in the room at the head of the stairs, Jeff," said Mrs. Davis.

"All right, Mamma," said Jeff. He turned to Howell. "Follow me," he said. "It's this way." The two boys went inside and started up the steps.

"Have you ever been to Kentucky before?" asked Jeff. All day long he had been thinking of the exciting trip that Major Hinds and his family soon would be taking.

"No," said Howell. "I'm anxious to go there, though. We're going to stop to see General Andrew Jackson on the way."

"General Jackson!" exclaimed Jeff. He'd often heard his older brothers talk of the famous hero of the War of 1812.

"Papa knew him during the war," said Howell.

The boys were almost at the top of the stairs. "Do you have a horse?" Howell asked suddenly.

"I surely do," said Jeff. "His name is Riptide of Rosemont, but I call him Rip. Was that your horse you were riding?"

"Yes," said Howell proudly. "I just got him before we started. Papa gave him to me."

By this time the boys had reached Howell's room. While the young guest was washing up,

Jeff told him all about the things he and James Pemberton and Rip did. Howie told Jeff about the trip from Natchez.

"I didn't get tired of riding," he said. "Papa says we have to get used to riding all day, so we'll be ready to go to Kentucky."

"I don't believe I'd ever get tired of riding." said Jeff.

Just then a voice called from downstairs. "Mister Jeff, you and Mister Howell come on down now. Your supper's on the table, and the other children already are sitting down."

Jeff stuck his head out the door and called, "We're coming, Serena!" He turned back to the room. "Come on, Howie," he said.

"All right," said Howie. He slicked down his hair with his hand. "I'm really hungry."

"So am I," said Jeff.

By the time supper was over, Jeff and Howie felt like old friends.

Off to Kentucky

THE LONG summer days seemed to fly by as Jeff and Howie played together. They spent hours riding their horses and caring for them. They played games. They climbed trees. They swam in the creek. James Pemberton often played with them.

One day when Major Hinds and his party had been at Rosemont about two weeks, Mr. Davis called Jeff aside. "Son," he said, putting his hand on Jeff's shoulder, "how would you like to go to Kentucky with the Major?"

"Oh, Papa!" exclaimed Jeff. "To Kentucky! May I take Rip?"

His father smiled. "Yes, you may. Kentucky is very far away. Your mother and I find it hard to think of your being so far away, but you must go to a good school. I've made arrangements for you to enter a fine school in Kentucky. Major Hinds will take you there. We will miss you very much, son, but we feel you must go."

Jeff threw his arms around his father. "I'll miss you, too, Papa, and Mamma and Anna and everybody! I'm so glad to get to go to Kentucky though. I've been wanting to go ever since Anna first told me the Major and his family were going there. May I tell Howie?"

"Yes," said Mr. Davis. "I'm glad you're anxious to go, Jeff." He stood watching his youngest son, as he happily ran off in search of Howie.

Both Mr. and Mrs. Davis hated the thought of their beloved seven-year-old son going so far away. "We'll miss him very much," thought Mr. Davis, "but he must go to a good school."

The next two weeks were busy ones. It seemed to Jeff that his mother and Anna were sewing almost the whole time. They were trying to make enough clothes to last him the two years he would be in Kentucky.

"I wish I knew just how much you were going to grow," said Mamma. She held a shirt she was making against his shoulders.

"It seems to me that I'll never be able to use all these clothes," said Jeff, "even if I'm as big as Isaac when I come home!"

"Don't even talk about staying that long!" said his mother, throwing her arms around him and hugging him.

Jeff hugged her, too. There were times when Kentucky did seem very far away to him. "I hope Mamma doesn't cry," thought Jeff, "because, if she does, I'm afraid I will, too."

Most of the time, though, Jeff was counting the minutes until it was time to go. At last it was the day before they were to leave. All day the household was busy getting things ready. There were clothes to be packed, food to be cooked—so many things!

Early the next morning the group set out. Mamma, Anna, and most of the other members of the household, including James Pemberton, had told Jeff good-by the night before. Mrs. Davis thought it would be easier that way. So early this morning, Mr. Davis and Isaac were the only ones on hand to see the travelers off.

"Well, it's going to be quite a trip, my boy," said Mr. Davis, giving Jeff a hug.

"All of it will be through Indian territory!" exclaimed Jeff excitedly.

Isaac laughed. "Almost all of it anyway," he said. "There are few white settlements on the whole trail."

"Well, I hope we get to see some Indians, too," said Jeff.

"Let's mount," said Major Hinds. "We should get started if we want to reach Natchez by to-night."

Mr. Davis gave Jeff a tight hug. "Be good, my son," he said softly.

Isaac hugged Jeff, too. "Have a good trip, fellow," he said.

Jeff climbed slowly into his sadde. He almost wished he weren't going. "I'm glad Mamma and the girls aren't here now," he thought. "They'd cry, and so would I."

Jeff was glad Papa and Isaac were waving and smiling. It made it much easier.

Then suddenly it wasn't hard to be happy he was going. He was sitting on Rip, in line with all the others. He looked at Howie, sitting on his horse next to him.

"Good-by, Papa! Good-by, Isaac!" he called.

Major Hinds gave the signal, and the little party was off—off to Kentucky!

At the head of the procession was Major Hinds. He wasn't wearing his army uniform now. He was dressed for the trip in a rough brown outfit.

Next to Major Hinds rode his wife. A little behind them came Howie's Aunt Beulah and her daughter Elizabeth. After them rode Earline, their Negro maid. Then came Jeff and Howie. Behind them was Jim Henry, who was in charge of the pack mules that followed.

"I'll be glad when we get to Natchez," said Jeff. "I won't feel as if we're really starting until we get beyond Natchez. Right now I feel as though we're just on our way to Natchez instead of Kentucky."

"I know," said Howie. "I do, too."

At noon the group stopped under a big oak tree to eat lunch. Serena had packed a big picnic basket for them.

"Here, Jeff," said Major Hinds, "here's a drumstick for you."

"Thank you, sir," said Jeff. "Serena surely makes good fried chicken. I'm going to miss it."

Major Hinds quickly looked up from his chicken. He looked at Jeff carefully. Jeff saw him.

"I'm all right, Major Hinds," the boy said. "I'll miss everybody, but I'm not going to be homesick. I think going on this trip to Kentucky is about the most wonderful thing that could happen to me."

"Good boy, Jeff," said Major Hinds. "Tomorrow you'll feel as though we're really on our way."

"I can hardly wait," said Jeff.

The summer days were long. The group reached Natchez before dark.

"There's Joseph!" cried Jeff. "He rode out to meet us!" Jeff slapped his horse's side and rushed forward to meet his brother.

"Slow down, fellow," laughed Joseph as his

68

youngest brother raced to meet him. "You'll get to Nashville without ever stopping in Natchez!"

Joseph rode with the Major's party back to his house, where a fine supper was ready.

Jeff ate a big meal. "I didn't know how hungry I was until I saw all the good food on the table," he said to Joseph. He had just finished a big piece of chocolate cake. Now he yawned.

"You don't know how sleepy you are, either," said Joseph, smiling. "Off to bed now. It'll be time to get up before you know it."

"You, too, Howie," said Mrs. Hinds.

The two boys told everyone good night. They went upstairs to get ready for bed. It was the end of their first full day of riding. As soon as Jeff's head touched the pillow, he was sound asleep.

On the Trace

Early the next morning the little party set out again. "Now we're really starting," he said to Howie. "We're on the Natchez Trace!"

Jeff had heard of the Natchez Trace all his life. It was the best-known trail from Natchez to Nashville.

Major Hinds heard him. "I hope you won't be disappointed in the Trace, Jeff," he said. "We probably won't see wild Indians, you know."

Jeff's face fell a little. He had hoped they'd see some wild Indians. He didn't want to see a scalping party, of course. He would like to see a brave creeping through the forest, though.

"The Trace is a post road now," continued Major Hinds. "The army helps to take care of it. Lots of people use it. We'll probably see fur traders, trappers——"

"No Indians at all?" Jeff interrupted.

Major Hinds smiled, "Oh, yes, we'll probably see some Indians, but they'll be friendly ones."

"Oh," said Jeff, "that's too bad." Still, friendly Indians would be better than no Indians at all.

The first day after leaving Joseph's plantation passed quickly. There were other people riding on the road from Natchez. There were a few people who passed them on their way from Nashville. It was late afternoon almost before Jeff knew it.

"Are we going to camp out tonight, sir?" asked Jeff excitedly. He knew there were rest cabins, or "stands," along the road for travelers to use.

"Yes," said Major Hinds. "We won't try to reach a stand tonight. The ladies aren't used to such constant riding. They're tired. We'll camp out instead."

Jeff turned to Howie. "I'm glad your father didn't say he was going slow because of us. I'm not a bit tired. Are you?"

"Of course not," said Howie.

The two boys looked at the roadside carefully. Suddenly Jeff called, "There's a clearing up ahead, sir!"

"So there is, Jeff," said Major Hinds. "Suppose you and Howie ride forward and see whether it will be a good place to camp."

Jeff and Howie urged their horses on. In a minute, they were in the clearing.

"This looks like a good place, doesn't it?" asked Jeff. "Look, there's the river right down there."

The whole space between the trail and the Mississippi River was clear. It was a space large enough for several camping parties.

The rest of the group soon reached the clearing. Major Hinds agreed that the clearing would be a good camp site. Everyone went to work. The pack mules were unloaded. The things needed for the night were unpacked.

"We'll need some wood," said Major Hinds. "Boys, you gather some small branches. There should be some near the edge of the clearing. We'll use some to put under the bedding to keep it dry. Earline will need some wood for the fire, too."

"Yes, sir," said Jeff and Howie together. Off they went. Jeff led the way among the tall trees. Soon he and Howie each had an armload of small branches. They took them back to the clearing. Then they made several more trips.

"There's a little stream just over the first rise in the woods, sir," said Jeff to Major Hinds.

"That's fine," the Major replied. "We can get our drinking water there. Does the stream look as though it might have fish in it?" he asked.

"Yes, sir," said Jeff.

"Oh, Papa, does that mean we can go fishing?" Howie asked.

"I think so," said Major Hinds. "Jim Henry's already found some worms for us. He thought there must be a good fishing stream near by."

Major Hinds finished dividing the branches Jeff and Howie had gathered. He had put the small ones in several piles. They would keep the bedding off the damp ground. The large branches would be used for the fire. Earline was starting to get things together for supper.

"Hurry and catch some fish now," said Mrs. Hinds. "It would be nice to have some for supper."

"We'll try," said Major Hinds. "Come on, Jim Henry. We'll have to teach these boys how to fish Indian-style."

"What's that?" asked Jeff.

"We'll show you, Mister Jeff," said Jim Henry,

smiling. By this time the Major, Jim, and the boys had reached the rise in the ground that bordered the creek.

"Cut off a few branches of that thorn bush over there for us, will you please, Jim?" asked Major Hinds.

"Yes, sir," said Jim Henry.

"Won't those branches be too short to use for poles, Papa?" asked Howie.

"We've already cut some cane reeds for poles, son," answered Major Hinds. "You'll see very soon why we want those thorn branches."

"I wonder if we're going to use them for hooks," said Jeff to Howie.

"It seems to me the thorns would break easily," said Howie.

"I think they would, too, but maybe the Indians have figured out some way to use them. Anyway, I guess we'll soon find out."

Just then Jim came back with the branches.

Major Hinds reached over to take one. "Ouch!" he exclaimed. "They surely are prickly."

"Here, Jim Henry, we'll each start on a hook. We'll show the boys how to make these first ones. Then they can make their own."

Major Hinds and Jim Henry started cutting off pieces of the branch.

"Oh," said Jeff, "you've cut your thorn off the branch, Jim Henry. I thought it made a nice hook just the way it was."

"It might have been pretty good that way," answered Jim Henry, "but this way's better. Now watch."

He cut a long thorn off. He took a piece of strong string from his pocket. Holding the thorn at an angle from the branch, he wound the string around it many times. He tied it.

"Now I see," said Jeff. "That makes a much stronger hook than a thorn growing out of a branch would make."

"That's right," said Jim Henry, "but we're not through. You could use it just this way as a hook, but it would be pretty easy for your fish to slip off."

Jim cut another thorn in two. Taking the sharp end, he tied it to the top end of his branch hook.

"Now," he said, "we have a point at each end. The fish is caught on the big hook. When he tries to pull up and get away, the little hook holds him in place."

"That makes a fine fishhook," said Jeff. "Can I try to make one now?"

Jim nodded and smiled.

Jeff set to work. In a few minutes he had made a good hook. He turned to Howie.

"Have you finished yours yet?" asked Jeff.

"Not quite," said Howie. He worked a few more minutes. "Now," he said, holding up the finished hook.

"Fine," said Major Hinds. "We'll each make a few more. Then we'll start." The two men and two boys worked in silence for a few minutes.

"Now," said the Major, standing up, "that ought to be enough. Let's make the lines and poles ready. Then we'll spread out and start fishing."

The strings soon were tied to the long cane poles. The hooks were fastened to the lines. Each of the fishermen took some of the worms Jim Henry had dug earlier.

"May we start now?" asked Jeff. He was eager to begin.

Major Hinds smiled. "Yes," he said, "run on and catch our supper, Jeff."

"Yes, sir!" exclaimed Jeff. He ran down the bank of the creek. "This looks like a good place," he thought. Putting his worms and extra hooks beside him, he sat down. In a few seconds, his line was in the water.

Jeff leaned back to wait. Everything was very peaceful. Looking down the creek, Jeff could see Howie, Major Hinds, and Jim Henry. Each one sat quietly by himself, waiting. Everything in the whole world seemed to be still.

Then, somewhere far away, a bird sang.

"Red-eyed towhee, drink-your-tea," sang Jeff softly, imitating the bird's call. He often had heard the towhee's call at Rosemont. He was still listening for "Drink-your-teeeee, drink-your-teeee!" when he felt a jerk on his line.

Jeff sat up quickly. "It must be a big one," he thought excitedly. Carefully he started pulling his line. He could see the fish in the water. "It has green fins! Maybe it's a bass like the one Isaac caught last summer!"

Jeff started to pull the line from the water. Now he could see the fish's head. It was a big one—lively, too! The fish wriggled and turned.

Just as Jeff pulled it from the water, the fish

twisted loose from the hook. It fell back into the water. *Splash!* "Oh-h-h-h!" said Jeff. He was disappointed.

Quickly Jeff put a new hook on the line, baited it, and threw it into the water. "I'll catch that fish this time," he thought. He sat back down to wait. He looked down the stream at the others. Howie was coming toward him.

"Look, Jeff!" cried Howie. "I've caught three bluegills. Look!" He held up a string of three small fish.

"That's fine, Howie," said Jeff. "Those will be good to eat. I haven't caught anything yet, but there's a big fellow here I'm going to catch."

Howie squatted beside Jeff. "He's nibbling," whispered Jeff, as his line jerked. "Every time I pull, though, he lets go."

The two boys were quiet for a few minutes. "There he goes again," said Jeff. He pulled in the line. The bait was gone.

"You'd better move downstream and try a new spot," said Howie. "That fish might be too big and too smart to get caught."

Jeff laughed. "That's not what's worrying me," he said. "I'm afraid he won't be hungry any more if he keeps eating my worms!" Once again Jeff baited his hook and threw it into the water.

Almost at once there was a little tug on the line. Jeff pulled the line just a little and stopped. There was another tug. Once more Jeff slowly pulled on the line. Again there was a tug. Both boys began to get excited.

Slowly, very slowly, Jeff pulled the line toward him. "Come on, Jeff!" whispered Howie. "You've just about got it now!"

Jeff pulled steadily and evenly. He was careful not to jerk the line. "I can still feel the fish nibbling," he whispered to Howie.

"I wish we had a net," Howie whispered back. "Then we would be sure to get it."

Jeff nodded. He was too busy to say anything. Suddenly there was a strong pull on the line. Jeff jerked his pole up into the air. There was his fish, swinging from the end of the line! Jeff was so excited he could hardly take the big bass off the hook.

Howie's eyes were wide with amazement. "That's almost the biggest fish I've ever seen!" he said.

"It's not the biggest one I've ever seen, but it's surely the biggest one I've ever caught!" replied Jeff.

"Let's go show Papa and Jim Henry," said Howie.

The two boys ran down the creek bank. Jeff was in front, carrying his fish and his pole. Howie ran close behind. They got to Jim Henry first.

"Look, Jim Henry!" shouted Howie. "Look what Jeff caught!"

"My!" said Jim Henry, "that's really a nice

one, Mister Jeff." He took Jeff's line and moved it up and down a time or two. He was trying to guess what the fish weighed. "This fellow must weigh about four pounds. That's a pretty good size for a bass."

Just then Major Hinds came up.

"Look, Papa," said Howie. "Look at Jeff's fish."

"Well, isn't that a fine catch!" said Major Hinds. "I saw you boys running and figured you'd caught something interesting. He started to put down his own string of fish.

"I'll hold them for you, sir," said Jeff. "Oh, you've caught a lot—six of them.

"I found a good place for bluegills," the Major said, "but your bass is the catch of the day, Jeff."

"It surely is, Mister Jeff," added Jim Henry.

"Thank you," said Jeff. He was grinning from ear to ear. He didn't think he'd ever been so proud before.

"Let's go back to camp now," suggested the Major. "We should have a good fish supper to-night."

Jim Henry agreed and picked up his own string of five bluegills.

Jeff and Howie walked a little behind the two men. Each boy carried his own fish.

"If every day is like this one," said Jeff to Howie, "it will be a wonderful trip!"

Great Adventure

"It's almost too bad we'll have to stay at a stand tonight," Jeff remarked the next day. "I really enjoyed camping out last night, didn't you, Howie?"

"Yes, I did," said Howie, "but Papa said we'd get to a stand at just the right time today. In fact, I imagine we're almost there now."

"That looks like a clearing up ahead," said Jeff. The two boys were riding a little ahead of the rest of the group. Suddenly Jeff cried, "Look, Howie! Look!"

"Indians!" Howie cried.

In the clearing, not far from the stand itself,

stood a small group of Indian braves. Both boys were terrified. They turned at once and raced back to the party to tell the news.

"There're Indians at the stand, Major Hinds!" cried Jeff.

"They've probably scalped everybody! They're probably getting ready to burn the stand now!" shouted Howie.

"Maybe they're waiting to capture us, too," said Jeff. "We might have to fight them."

Major Hinds smiled. "I'm sorry to disappoint you young fighters, but these Indians are friendly. The white man who runs this stand is married to an Indian. Those Indians probably are members of her family. They probably came to sell food to the people who stop at the stand."

Jeff and Howie were a little disappointed, but they were delighted that they would get to see some Indians anyway. They rode toward the stand eagerly.

"We should be able to buy fresh deer meat from the Indians," Major Hinds told his wife. "Maybe we can buy a couple of wild turkeys, too."

The Indians stood near the large log cabin, or stand, where the travelers could spend the night. The stand owner and his wife provided beds, and they cooked for those who wanted to buy a hot supper.

"These Indians are members of the Choctaw

tribe," said the Major as the little party drew nearer to the stand. "They always have been friendly to white men. I'm going to try to buy some food from them now. Would you boys like to come?"

"Yes, sir!" said the two boys together.

While Major Hinds bargained with the Choctaws for the meat they had to sell, Jeff looked at the Indians closely. They were tall, quiet, and dignified. "They don't look or act like 'savages' at all," he thought.

Jeff saw many other new things to interest him on the trail in the days that followed. Often he saw deer. Sometimes he saw bears. Once in a while Major Hinds shot a deer for food, but he didn't shoot any bears.

"The bears won't bother us," said the Major. "Besides we aren't so short of food that we have to eat bear meat—though, of course, a great many people do."

90

Jeff's group often passed other travelers, for the Natchez Trace was a well-known trail.

"I think the travelers I like best are the keelboatmen," said Jeff one day.

"They are interesting," said Major Hinds. "They float down the river on their flatboats or keelboats. When they get to one of the Southern ports, usually Natchez or New Orleans, they sell their cargo. Then they have to walk back home. Their boats can only float downstream with the current. They can't go back under their own power."

The keelboatmen wore buckskins. Usually they were big husky fellows. "They look so strong," said Jeff. "It's easy to imagine them guiding their boats down the river."

"Guiding keelboats is hard work," said the Major. "The men use long poles to keep their boats from running into sandbars and driftwood. They have to be strong."

Day by day the travelers moved closer to Kentucky. Jeff had been a good rider before, but now he became a really fine young horseman. He no longer got tired after long hours in the saddle.

Jeff and Howie learned to make the beds when the party camped out. They could help Earline build her fire. They could help Jim Henry load and unload the mules.

Major Hinds told his wife, "The two boys really have become seasoned travelers now."

One morning Major Hinds said, "We're getting close to Nashville now. We'll be at the Hermitage soon."

"The Hermitage is the name of General Andrew Jackson's plantation," Howie explained.

"Oh," said Jeff. "I'll be glad to get there. I'm anxious to see General Jackson. Joseph, Benjamin, and Samuel often talked about him when they came home from the war."

"My papa fought under him at the Battle of New Orleans," said Howie proudly. "General Jackson was a great hero."

The little party was riding through a growth of beautiful trees. "We'll see the house just beyond these trees," the Major announced.

"I see it," cried Jeff a moment later. "I hear music, too."

Major Hinds smiled. "That's probably the General playing his flute," he said, "and Mrs. Jackson playing the spinet."

A few minutes later the riders dismounted before the large log house. A Negro servant in a white coat opened the door for them. Suddenly the music stopped. A tall, lean man with a great shock of red hair came quickly into the room.

"Major Hinds!" the tall man exclaimed, thrusting out his hand as he rushed forward. "What a pleasure!"

Then he eagerly greeted the rest of the party.

He seemed very much pleased when he heard that they would be visiting the Hermitage for several weeks.

"I'm glad, too," said Howie to Jeff. "It will be nice to stay in a house again."

"Especially in a house with General Jackson," Jeff added. "I like him already."

The weeks that followed were happy ones for Jeff. Andy Jackson, Jr., the General's adopted son, showed Jeff and Howie all around the plantation. They had lots of fun together.

One morning the three boys had been playing in the woods. Now they were walking back toward the house. Suddenly Jeff said, "Look! I see a couple of horses on the road. They're coming this way!"

Andy and Howie looked.

"It's probably somebody coming to see Papa," said Andy.

"I've never known anyone who has so many

visitors as your father," said Jeff. "At home we have guests only once in a while. They're always relatives or old family friends. Here, folks come by all the time."

"It seems to me there are new faces at supper every night," put in Howie.

"It's been that way ever since the end of the war," said Andy. "Lots of people stop by just to meet Papa. Many of the old soldiers who fought under him stop to visit with us, too."

"I think I'd like to be a soldier and fight under General Jackson when I grow up," Jeff said.

"So would I," agreed Howie.

The boys were close enough now to see the hitching post in front of the house. "Those horses belong to the Parkers," Andy said. "They live on the next plantation. James and Richard come over to play sometimes. They must be here now."

The three boys hurried inside. Mrs. Jackson

was just greeting the two Parker boys. "How nice to have you, James and Richard. I'm glad your mother let you visit while Jeff and Howie are here."

"How very friendly General and Mrs. Jackson are," thought Jeff. "They make everybody feel right at home."

Soon afterward, General Jackson and Major Hinds came in. Everyone went into the dining room for dinner.

After everyone had been seated, General Jack-

son said, "What have you been doing lately, Richard? Is there any news from the Parker household?"

"We've been taking care of our horses the last few days, sir. James has a new saddle, and he thinks he can ride better than Papa now." Richard grinned at his younger brother.

"I see," said the General with a smile. "Well, why don't we have a race this afternoon? We can find out who can ride fastest, if not best. With Jeff, Howie, Andy, and now Richard and James, we should have a pretty fair race. Would you be interested?"

"Yes, sir!" answered the five boys, all speaking at once.

"Major Hinds and I will go out and mark a course after dinner. We'll use some of the wagon trails out to the fields," said the General.

At last it was time for the race. The boys hurried to get their horses.

"Here's the line, boys," said General Jackson. "Line your horses up here. When Major Hinds fires his pistol, you'll start! I'm going down to the finish line now. "I'll be the judge to see who wins."

The General walked down to the finish line where Mrs. Jackson, Mrs. Hinds, Howie's Aunt Beulah, and his cousin Elizabeth were gathered. They had come out to watch the race, too.

Jeff sat on Rip, waiting for the starting gun. His heart was beating rapidly. "Rip's such a wonderful horse," he thought. "I surely wish we could win. Then everybody could see how fast he can run!"

Bang! Major Hinds fired his pistol. The five horses shot forward.

"Come on, Rip—come on, boy!" shouted Jeff. Now Jeff pulled just a little ahead of Andy and Richard. Just in front of them was James. He was riding as hard as he could on his new saddle.

"Come on, boy—faster, faster!" yelled Jeff. Jeff passed James.

Howie was leading the field, but Jeff caught up with him! Neck and neck they rode. The air was filled with the noise of the racers' shouts, the thud of the horses' hoofs on the hard dirt, and the cheers of the watching crowd.

"Now, boy! Now, Rip! Just a little more—a little faster!" urged Jeff.

The five riders dashed across the finish line. Jeff and Howie were ahead, with the other three riders close behind. Jeff wasn't sure who had won. Then he heard General Jackson shout, "Davis wins, with Hinds a very close second!"

Jeff leaped from his saddle. He threw both arms around Rip's neck. "We did it, Rip! We did it!" he cried.

Everyone crowded around Jeff and Howie, laughing and talking. They shook the boys' hands and patted the panting horses.

100

"Now," said Mrs. Jackson, "let's go inside. Our racers need some refreshment after that hard ride. Jeff shall have the biggest piece of cake!"

Jeff laughed. "It should go to Rip, Mrs. Jackson," he said, "but I don't suppose he'd like it half as much as I would. So I'll just have to eat it for him!"

Steamboating down the River

CLOTHES to pack, books to pack, everything to pack! Jeff was going home. After two years at school in Kentucky, he would soon be on his way back to Mississippi.

"I'll miss all of my friends here," thought Jeff, as he packed his clothes, "but I can hardly wait to get home again!"

The family had written Jeff about the things that were happening at home, of course. They had written about Anna's wedding and Benjamin's wedding. They had written about the new horses that had been bought and the new plantation buildings that had been built.

"I'll have so many things to catch up with," thought Jeff. "It's been a long time since James Pemberton and I have run down to the stables together to see Rip." Major Hinds had taken Rip back to Rosemont when he and his family returned to Mississippi.

"I hope Rip hasn't forgotten me," thought Jeff.

The last two days of Jeff's stay at the Kentucky school were very busy. There was so much to do. Jeff was sure he wouldn't have time to do everything that had to be done. Even so, the time dragged by.

"I think these last two days have been longer than the whole two years that I've been away from home," Jeff told one of his classmates.

The night before he was to leave, Jeff sat at the front gate of the school. He was waiting for Charles Green. Charles was a young man from Mississippi who had been studying law in Kentucky. He had acted as Jeff's guardian while the boy was away from home. Now he was going to take care of Jeff on the trip home.

"Hello, Charles!" Jeff called, when the tall young man rode up. Jeff liked Charles very much. He was glad they would be traveling together.

"Hello, Jeff," said Charles, swinging down from his big horse. "Are you ready to travel?"

"I think so," Jeff replied.

"I have some good news for you," said Charles. "We're going home by steamboat!"

"Steamboat!" cried Jeff. "Wait till I tell the boys here at school!"

Jeff's announcement caused quite a bit of excitement. Everyone at school had been interested in Jeff's long trip to Kentucky. Most of the boys had taken long horseback rides but none so long as Jeff's trip.

Now Jeff was going home on a steamboat! This news made the long horseback trip seem almost like an everyday event. No one at school even knew anyone who had been on a steamboat!

Jeff told everyone good-by that night after supper. He was the youngest boy in school. Everyone liked him and hated to see him go. Jeff was sorry to leave his friends, too, but he was eager to start for home. That night he dreamed of Rosemont and steamboats and Rip and the school—all mixed together.

Early the next morning Jeff and Charles set out. They were going to a town built beside the Falls of the Ohio. The steamboats came up the Mississippi River and then up the Ohio River.

As the two travelers drew near to the town, they noticed that the road was crowded.

"My goodness," said Jeff, "it looks as though everybody's going our way."

"There surely are lots of people on the road," said Charles. "We'll stop at Miles's Livery Stable, Jeff. That's where I rented our horses."

"I've never been to a livery stable," said Jeff.

"A livery stable looks like almost any other stable," said Charles. "People can rent all kinds of horses and carriages there."

Moments later the two riders came to the stable. Jeff was ready to dismount and hitch his horse to the post outside. Charles rode right into the stable, though, so Jeff followed.

Jeff gave his horse to a stableman. Then he began to look at the saddles. Charles said, "We've paid for everything, Jeff. Let's go."

Jeff and Charles walked out into the sunshine and started through the streets toward the wharves. There were many people on the streets.

"Everybody seems to be going to the river, too," remarked Jeff.

"I guess most of them want to see the steamboat," Charles said. "People come from miles away just to see one."

As Jeff and Charles drew closer to the wharves,

they saw more and more people. A large crowd had gathered to watch the boat leave. "It feels just like the Fourth of July," thought Jeff.

There was a holiday-like excitement in the air. Little boys sat on their fathers' shoulders to get a better look at the strange boat. People moved this way and that, trying to see over the heads of the people in front of them. There was a steady hum of excited talk.

Several well-dressed ladies and gentlemen

were boarding the steamboat for a few hours' ride.

"I can see it!" cried Jeff. "I can see the steamboat!"

"I can see the name of the boat," said Charles. "It's the 'Aetna.'"

How busy and important the steamboat looked! Her huge paddle wheel glistened with water and sunshine. Her big steam boilers glowed red with flame. Her tall smokestack sent up clouds of heavy black smoke.

Jeff thought the "Aetna" was a wonderful sight, indeed, as he and Charles hurried toward her through the crowd.

"Pardon me, sir," said Charles, as he tried to make his way forward. "We must get aboard the steamboat."

People stepped aside immediately. Several men turned to look at these new steamboat passengers. Jeff felt very important.

108

In a few minutes Jeff and Charles were walking up the gangplank. Everything on the boat was exciting.

There were other passengers, like Jeff and Charles, getting on board with boxes and packages. Ladies in feathered bonnets and fringed shawls leaned against the rail, waving to friends on shore.

Some men carried the last of the cargo aboard. Other men carried wood, which they stacked in huge piles next to the furnaces.

"Those are the biggest fireplaces I've ever seen!" exclaimed Jeff.

"Those are the furnaces," Charles explained. "They heat the water that becomes the steam that makes the boat move."

"Who's that man?" Jeff asked when he saw an important-looking figure in a blue uniform with gold braid on it.

"That's the captain," Charles replied. "Do

you see the brass spyglass under his arm and the speaking trumpet in his hand?"

Jeff nodded.

"He calls out his orders through that speaking trumpet," Charles went on. "The Captain is an important man. His name is Robinson DeHart."

"Even his name sounds important," laughed Jeff.

Just then Captain DeHart lifted his speaking trumpet. "All aboard!" he shouted. "All aboard!"

There was a last minute rush. The gangplank was lifted. The anchor was weighed. Three great puffs of smoke shot upward from the smokestack. They were followed by a steady stream of black smoke. A shrill whistle blew.

Slowly the great paddle wheel began to turn. Then it began to turn faster and faster.

"We're moving!" shouted Jeff.

A cheer went up from the crowd. The whistle blew again. The "Aetna" was on its way!

110

Jeff was standing at the rail a few hours later when Charles came up. "Still watching the paddle wheel, Jeff?" Charles asked. He leaned over the rail to watch, too.

"Yes, sir," replied the boy. "I like the way it churns up the water. It leaves a white trail behind us, like a little road."

"It reminds me of the train of a girl's white ball gown," Charles said.

Jeff didn't know about a girl's ball gown, but he did think the white foamy trail was pretty. Just then he felt a change in the boat's motion. "Why, it feels as though we're slowing down," he said.

The crew hurried all about the boat. Captain DeHart called orders through his speaking trumpet again. Slowly, the "Aetna" turned toward the bank.

"We're going toward shore!" exclaimed Jeff. "Why are we stopping so soon, Charles?"

"I guess this is where some of the passengers are getting off," Charles replied.

"Look at all the carriages!" Jeff exclaimed.

Eight large carriages lined the road near a large plantation house which faced the river. Coachmen stood about in little groups. As they watched the arrival of the steamboat, they talked and pointed excitedly.

The coachmen were waiting for the people who had taken a short ride on the "Aetna." Most of these people lived near the Falls of the Ohio. Now they would ride home in their carriages.

The steamboat pulled up to the small plantation pier. Jeff watched with interest as the elegant ladies and gentlemen left the boat. He could hear some of their talk as they went down the gangplank.

"Did you see all that black smoke and flame pouring out of the smokestack?" asked one lady. "I was quite frightened."

"So was I," said her companion, "but it was thrilling to watch that huge paddle wheel turning so fast."

A large, well-dressed man passed near Jeff. "It was an experience I shall never forget," the man said to a friend.

Jeff thought to himself, "This is an experience I shall never forget, either."

The boy watched the men and women climb into their carriages. In a few minutes the steamboat was on its way once more.

The "Aetna" stopped many times on the long journey southward. Jeff enjoyed these breaks in the trip very much.

Often the boat stopped to take on fresh water. Sometimes she tied up near a wooded section of the riverbank. Jeff watched the crew go ashore and cut wood. The wood was used for fuel in the boilers.

Captain DeHart would stand on the deck,

shouting orders to the crewmen on shore. The gold braid on his uniform would flash in the sun. Then the Captain would look down the river through his brass spyglass. Jeff admired the tall captain of the "Aetna."

Jeff also enjoyed watching one of the crewmen who did the sounding. This man would stand in the front of the boat and throw a lead weight into the water. The weight was attached to a long line that had been marked off.

As the weight sank into the water, it would draw the line under, too. When the weight hit the river bottom, the crewman would notice how much of the line had gone into the water. In this way, he knew how deep the river was in this place.

"It looks pretty deep here, doesn't it?" asked Jeff one day, as he watched the sounding line pay out.

"It does," the crewman replied. "Ah, there's the floor," he said, as he felt the line go slack. The weight had hit the river bottom.

"It'll be easy sailing here," the sailor continued, "but soon we'll be getting to a part of the river where the water is no deeper than a duck pond."

"When do you think we'll get to that part of the river?" Jeff asked.

"We'll probably be getting into shallow water along about tomorrow evening—maybe earlier," the man replied.

The next afternoon Jeff was lying on his stomach on the deck near the paddle wheel. His chin was in his hands. He was watching the wheel churn the water to white foam as it spun around.

It was not long after dinner, and the sun was warm. Several of the passengers were taking naps. The whole steamboat had a rather sleepy air.

Suddenly there was a loud *wham!* Jeff was thrown hard against the side rail, as the boat came to a sudden, shaking stop.

Jeff felt himself slipping over the side. Dazed as he was, the boy tried to grab the rail. He heard someone scream, "We've run aground!" Just then Jeff's grip on the rail slipped. He felt himself falling.

Splash! Jeff hit the water hard. Then he disappeared beneath the surface of the river.

"Man overboard!" a sailor cried.

116

The boat burst into activity. Members of the crew came running from all directions. The passengers, jolted awake from their naps, rushed to the side of the boat. They peered over the rail, trying to see who had fallen overboard.

As Jeff felt the brown water close over his head, he immediately began to kick and paddle. In the long second that it took him to rise to the surface, Jeff was aware of a heavy noise in the water.

"What is that roar?" he asked himself. Then he knew. "The paddle wheel! I must get away from the paddle wheel or I'll be drawn into it."

Just then Jeff's head broke water. In an instant he took in the scene. Anxious passengers and crewmen crowded against the "Aetna's" rail, looking down at him. He heard Charles shouting, "I'm coming, Jeff! I'm coming!" Jeff could see his friend taking off his shoes.

Then Jeff heard Captain DeHart shouting

through his speaking trumpet. "Stop the wheel! Stop the wheel!"

Jeff felt himself being sucked toward the turning, churning paddle wheel. He tried to swim harder, but the water pulled against his legs. He kicked harder. He thrust his arms through the foamy water and pulled with all his might.

Just then the great wheel stopped turning, and Jeff shot forward suddenly. Now Charles was beside him in the water. Jeff had been so busy that he hadn't seen Charles leap into the water.

"Hold on to me, Jeff," said Charles. "There are only a few more yards to go."

"I think I can make it, Charles," the boy replied.

Jeff was very tired. He was worn out from his struggle against the paddle wheel's pull. Still, he was close to the boat. So he insisted on swimming the rest of the way by himself.

In another minute, Captain DeHart and the crew members were hauling Jeff and Charles aboard the "Aetna."

"A fine show of courage and skill, my boy," boomed Captain DeHart. He always spoke as though he were making an announcement through his speaking trumpet.

Passengers and sailors patted Jeff on the back. They all told him how well he had done. Jeff thanked them, but he was very glad when he and Charles finally got to their room.

They had just taken off their wet clothes and were putting on dry ones when there was a knock on their cabin door.

"Come in," said Charles.

It was Captain DeHart. "I thought you boys might like to know that the jolt that threw Jeff overboard wasn't so bad as it might have been."

"Didn't we run aground?" asked Jeff.

The Captain smiled. "No, we didn't run

aground. We hit the side of a sandbar and are barely sitting on its edge. We'll have the boat off that edge in a matter of minutes."

Jeff turned to Charles. "May I go watch?" the boy asked.

Charles laughed. "I guess so," he said, shaking his head. "I think I'll have to stay here and rest a while, though. *I've* just had a tiring swim." Then Charles laughed again.

Life on the "Aetna"

WHEN Jeff and Captain DeHart went back out on deck, most of the passengers and crew were still standing along the rail. Many of them spoke to Jeff and complimented him for his courage. Some of them patted him on the back as he went up to the rail to join them.

Everyone was watching the preparations to move the steamboat off the edge of the sandbar. Jeff watched as several crew members brought long poles.

"Please move aside," the sailors said. The passengers moved over to make room for the sailors at the rail. Captain DeHart shouted orders through his speaking trumpet and waved his spyglass.

One passenger standing near Jeff turned to his neighbor. "One would think," he said, "that we were in the middle of the Atlantic Ocean!"

They both laughed. The second man replied, "Captain DeHart was a real sea-going sailor in his younger days, and he's never forgotten his experiences."

The crew members started to push against the sandbar with their long poles. At first, it seemed they weren't going to move the boat at all. Captain DeHart called for more men and more poles.

"Maybe we're farther on the sandbar than the Captain thought," said Jeff to himself.

Other crew members appeared with more poles. In a few minutes poles sprouted from the whole side of the boat.

"The poles look just like a porcupine's bristles," thought Jeff.

"At the count of three, all will push together," the Captain shouted. Now he lowered the speaking trumpet a second, took a deep breath, and raised it to his mouth again. "One, two, three—push!" he shouted.

Everyone pushed. The "Aetna" shuddered slightly. Then, suddenly, she spurted forward—free.

"Hooray!" cried the passengers.

"Hooray!" cried Jeff. The "Aetna" was on her way once more.

Besides such unscheduled stops as the one caused by the sandbar, the steamboat made regular stops, too. Cargo was loaded and unloaded at many places along the river.

Jeff particularly enjoyed the stop at Fort Massacre. The river stretched a mile wide at that point. "I feel as though I can see a hundred miles down the river," Jeff said.

Charles laughed. "Well, I'm sure you can't

see quite that far, but one can see quite a distance. Here comes Captain DeHart now. Let's ask him."

Charles called, "Captain, Jeff and I have been wondering how far down the river one can see from this point. It seems unusually far."

"It is, indeed," replied Captain DeHart. "One can see fourteen miles down the river at this point—if he has good eyes."

"Fourteen miles," repeated Charles. "Well, that really is a distance."

"Now, with my spyglass I can see much farther," the Captain put in. He saw Jeff looking longingly at the telescope. "Would you like to have a look through a real spyglass, my boy?" he asked.

"Yes, sir!" Jeff answered eagerly.

Carefully he took the spyglass and looked at the shoreline a mile away. Then he looked miles down the river.

"Everything looks so much bigger," he said,
putting down the telescope a minute. He raised
it again. "I can see so many things I can't see at
all without the spyglass. Thank you very much,
sir," he said, returning the glass to Captain
DeHart.

"You're welcome, my boy," said the Captain.
"You may look again sometime."

Jeff was delighted. He had liked looking

through the glass. He had felt as though he were a real captain, sailing the seven seas and scanning the shore for pirates and hidden treasure!

A few days later Jeff almost saw some pirates. The "Aetna" was moving along at a steady pace. Jeff was walking idly along the deck. It was such a nice morning that he whistled as he went along.

When he reached the forward deck of the ship, he noticed several of the passengers gathered together. They were standing in a little group near the rail, looking off at the shoreline. Charles was with them, so Jeff went over to ask what was happening.

"What's everyone looking at, Charles?" he asked. "We aren't going to run aground again, are we?"

"Oh, no," said Charles. "No danger of that. Everyone's looking at that big rock over there on the other side of the river. It's Cave-in-Rock.

A gang of thieves and robbers meet there. Often they have slipped out from their stronghold there and attacked passing boats."

"Pirates!" said Jeff, excitedly. "They're river pirates, but they're real pirates just the same!"

"They surely are," said Charles, "and just as mean as any ocean pirates. I hope we don't meet any of them," he added.

"Well, I really wouldn't want us to meet any," said Jeff, scanning the shore. He stood with the other passengers and watched as long as Cave-in-Rock was in view.

Talking to Charles later, he said, "I'm glad the pirates didn't come after the "Aetna," of course. You would think, though, we'd have seen at least one pirate moving around in the distance, wouldn't you?"

While Jeff didn't get to see any pirates, he did see many other interesting people on the trip. Whenever the "Aetna" tied up at any of the river settlements, Jeff leaned over the rail of the boat and looked at the people who crowded around the wharf.

He saw hunters in dirty buckskins. Often wild turkeys hung from their belts.

Jeff saw Indians, too. They came to the riverbanks with deer meat to sell. Jeff would watch while Captain DeHart bought game from the Indians for the "Aetna's" crew and passengers.

These Indians were usually tall, clean, and healthy in appearance. Jeff noticed that they often seemed to have an air of honor and dignity that many of the white settlers along the riverbank did not.

After the "Aetna" had left the Ohio River, it entered the Mississippi. Now the steamboat traveled faster. The Mississippi River itself ran faster than the Ohio. Jeff heard Captain DeHart say that the current alone went as fast as four miles an hour.

Some days, Jeff and Charles watched the shore for hours at a time. As the boat steamed farther southward, Jeff began to notice plants and trees that he had seen around Woodville. Charles pointed out the different trees and plants and birds to Jeff. He taught the boy the names of the birds and trees.

One day, as Jeff was watching the shore slip by, he saw something that excited him more than anything on the whole trip.

"Look, Charles," Jeff cried. "Look! I can see the bluffs." He pointed to the high, steep banks that rose up from the river's edge. "We must be nearing Natchez. We must be almost home!"

Home Again

THE NEXT day Jeff stayed near the deck railing as though he were glued to it. Finally he saw what he had been waiting for. "Look, Charles!" he cried. "There's Natchez-under-the-Hill! We're really here at last!"

Charles joined the boy at the rail. He was excited, too. "You know, Jeff," he said, "even Natchez-under-the-Hill looks good to me today. And look at all the people!"

Natchez-under-the-Hill was a village by the side of the river. The town of Natchez was built high above the river. Usually the good citizens of Natchez stayed away from this village when they could. It was considered a den of thieves and gamblers.

Today, however, many people who normally wouldn't be there had come to see the "Aetna." The steamboat was, of course, as much of a curiosity to these people as it had been to the people of Kentucky. A large crowd had gathered.

As the "Aetna" pulled in close to the wharf, Jeff started searching the crowd. "Isaac must be there somewhere," he thought. "Mamma wrote that he would meet me. Of course, Joseph will be here, too. I wonder where they are."

Suddenly Jeff saw his brothers in the crowd. He leaned so far forward that Charles reached over to catch his jacket. "Whoa!" he said. "Don't fall overboard again!"

Jeff didn't even hear him. He was too busy waving and shouting, "Joseph! Isaac! Here!"

The brothers both saw him at the same instant. They waved excitedly to him.

132

Moments later the steamboat docked. Jeff ran down the gangplank with Charles close behind. He threw himself into the open arms of his brothers.

"Oh, Joseph!" he said. "Isaac!" He hugged one and then the other. Oh, how happy he was to see them!

"How you've grown, Jeff!" exclaimed Joseph. He stepped back to take a better look at him. "You're twice as big as you were when you left!" he said.

"Indeed you are," said Isaac. "You must have grown a foot!"

"Well, I don't believe I've grown quite that much," said Jeff, "but I outgrew all the clothes I took with me. I've outgrown many of the things Mamma and Anna sent me, too."

"I don't doubt that," said Joseph. "Let's get in the carriage. You can tell us all about your trip on the 'Aetna' while we ride to the house.

We've never talked to anyone who has traveled on a steamboat, you know."

Jeff talked almost the whole way to Joseph's house. When they arrived, Joseph turned to Isaac and said, "You know, I believe our baby brother has not only grown quite a bit, but has also grown up."

Jeff thought he'd burst all the buttons off his shirt. Having his oldest brother say that made him feel very proud and happy.

Jeff and Isaac spent that night in Joseph's house near Natchez. "We'll leave early tomorrow. That way we'll have lots of time to cover those thirty-five miles to Rosemont," said Isaac.

"It'll be the longest thirty-five miles of the whole trip," said Jeff.

Early the next morning, Isaac and Jeff set out for Woodville. It was a fine day—sunny but not too hot for comfort.

134

"It's good to be on this old familiar road again," said Jeff. He noticed the blackberry bushes near the road. "How are the blackberries this year, Isaac? I haven't had any blackberries in two years. I'd like to have some."

"I believe it's supposed to be a good year for them," said Isaac. "I heard Mamma and Serena talking about making jelly the other day. In fact, I wouldn't be surprised if Mamma had blackberry cobbler for dessert tonight. She knows how much you like it."

"I hope so," said Jeff happily.

The two brothers rode on. They talked about the hunting Isaac had done the past two winters and the fishing they might do this summer. At noon they stopped under a tall magnolia tree to eat the delicious lunch they'd brought from Joseph's.

From time to time, Isaac said something about how much Jeff had grown. "I'm not sure I'd have recognized you if I hadn't known you were coming on that boat," he said.

Jeff laughed. "Maybe nobody at Rosemont will know me. They might think you're bringing home a new friend you found in Natchez."

Isaac laughed, too, and said, "Let's see if they recognize you. When we get to the bend in the road just before you get to the house, I'll stay behind. I'll hide behind the rose hedges while you go up to the house alone.

"Mamma will be watching near the front door, I know. She won't be able to see me, so she won't know we're together. We'll just see if she knows who you are when she sees you!"

"All right," said Jeff. He was getting quite excited now. In another minute he would be rounding the bend in the road. Beyond the bend lay the house at Rosemont and Mamma, Papa, and all the others."

"Let's stop here," said Isaac. "Leave your

136

horse here with me. Mamma might recognize it. You can pretend it ran away and you're looking for it."

Jeff dismounted and gave the reins to Isaac. Now the older brother tried to find a place to look through the hedge.

"I want to be able to see the house without Mamma's being able to see me," he explained.

Jeff pretended to be calm as he walked down the road toward the house. His heart was beating very fast indeed. Then he saw his mother sitting on the porch. "She's waiting for me!" he thought.

Jeff was really excited now, but he pretended to be a stranger. He walked toward the house, looking around as though he were hoping to see his horse near by. "Excuse me, ma'am," he said, as he neared the porch steps, "I was just traveling by, and I seem to have lost my horse. Have you seen any stray horses anywhere around?"

"No," said Mrs. Davis, rushing down the steps, "but I do see a stray boy!"

Mamma gathered Jeff in her arms. Jeff threw both his arms around her neck. They clung together for a long moment. Oh, how wonderful it was to be home again!

When they were a little calmer, Jeff asked, "Where is Papa?"

"He's checking on things in the south field," said his mother. "Why don't you go down and surprise him right now?"

By this time Isaac had ridden up to the house. "Please give me my horse, Isaac," cried Jeff. "I'm going out to see Papa."

Mr. Davis sat astride his big black horse, watching the field hands work. He was a quiet man who seldom let people know what he was feeling, but Jeff took him by surprise.

"Jeff! Jeff, my boy!" he shouted, when he recognized the rider coming out to the field.

Both riders dismounted. Papa grabbed Jeff up in his arms and hugged him.

Jeff was surprised. "I don't think I've ever seen Papa so happy or excited before," he thought. "And I'm sure I've never been so happy or excited before either! Oh, it certainly is wonderful to be home again!"

The Twentieth State

THE SUMMER passed quickly—almost before Jeff knew it. Now it was fall and time for school again. Ever since Jeff had come home from Kentucky, his family had been discussing where he would go to school next.

"I guess Mr. McAllister's school is about the best choice," Mrs. Davis said. "It's close to Natchez, so Jeff can spend every week end with Joseph. And he'll be able to come here during the longer vacations."

"That will be fine," said Jeff. "It will be nice to be able to get home for holidays. I'll enjoy being able to see Joseph often, too."

Even though Joseph was twenty-three years older than Jeff, the two brothers were always very close. They always enjoyed being together.

"I like seeing Natchez, too," Jeff told Joseph one day. "There are always many carriages coming and going, and so many people walking and riding around downtown when we go there. I believe you know every one of them, too!"

Joseph laughed. It really did seem that everybody knew him.

"People are always stopping to speak to you about something or other every time we go downtown," Jeff went on.

"Well, most of them want to talk to me about politics," said Joseph. "Mississippi wants to become a state in the Union. I'm helping to write a constitution so she can become a state."

Joseph spent almost all of his time working on the project. Often when Jeff was visiting him on week ends, he would see Joseph for a few

142

hours only. Some of the most important men in Mississippi came to Joseph's house while Jeff was there. Sometimes Joseph introduced Jeff to them.

One Saturday afternoon, Jeff was in the sitting room in Joseph's house. He was doing his school-work for Monday. Joseph's wife, Eliza, was sewing. Suddenly Joseph burst into the room.

"We've done it!" he cried. "We've finished the constitution at last! Mississippi will be admitted to the Union!"

"That's wonderful, dear," said Eliza. She was as happy as Joseph.

"There's to be a big celebration," Joseph went on, "and do you know when it will be?"

"No, sir," said Jeff. "Will it be at Christmas?" It was November and everybody at school already was talking about the Christmas holidays.

"No, sir," replied Joseph. "Mississippi will become one of the United States of America on December 10, 1817. What do you think of that?"

"Why, Joseph, that's your birthday!" exclaimed Eliza. "How wonderful! We'll have to have a very special celebration."

"Did they pick your birthday on purpose?" asked Jeff.

"Why, of course they did," said Joseph, laughing. "Of course they did."

144

Jeff couldn't tell whether his brother was joking or not. He didn't have a chance to find out, because Joseph and Eliza started making plans right away.

"We'll want you to come, too, of course," Eliza said to Jeff.

"Certainly," put in Joseph. "I'll write Mr. McAllister at once to tell him that I want you to come here on the ninth and stay over until the eleventh. Then you can spend the whole day with us. Mississippi and I both will have to see that it's a great occasion. It'll be a day to tell your grandchildren about!"

"I don't know about grandchildren," said Jeff, "but I'll surely be glad to see it myself."

When Jeff arrived at Joseph's home bright and early on December ninth, preparations for the next day were already well under way.

Servants were polishing the floors. Servants were polishing the furniture. Servants were polishing the beautiful heavy silver in the dining-room cabinets.

"I think everybody is busy polishing every-thing that possibly can be polished!" Jeff thought.

Just then Eliza came into the room. "It's nice you arrived here early, Jeff. I'm doing a hun-dred things," she said. "I just finished checking with Missy in the kitchen to see how the prepara-tions are going in there.

"Right now I'm looking to see if there are flowers in all of the rooms. I think I still have to do one or two bouquets for the upstairs rooms."

"Everybody certainly looks busy," said Jeff.

"And in between all those things, I must have a last fitting of my ball gown," Eliza went on. "It must be ready for the birthday ball tomorrow evening. By the way, Joseph is outside, if you'd like to see him."

Jeff hurried outside. He found his older brother behind the kitchen.

146

"Hello, my boy," said Joseph when he saw Jeff.
"I'm just checking on the barbecue pits. If the
pits aren't dug properly, the meat won't cook
properly. Would you like to go with me to pick
out the meat?"

Jeff said he would. So he went with Joseph
to watch him pick out the very finest cuts of
beef to be used for the barbecue. A little later
they joined Eliza in the ballroom.

"This floor is quite slippery," said Jeff.

He slid across it a few times until Joseph said
maybe he'd better stop before it became too slippery. "We don't want any of our guests falling
down right in the middle of a dance."

Jeff went to bed early that night. He wanted
to wake up at the crack of dawn. "I don't want
to miss a single thing!" he thought.

He needn't have worried about oversleeping,
though. At daybreak a huge *boom* almost
bounced him out of bed.

Jeff rushed to a window and looked out. There was a flash of fire by the parade grounds as another great *boom* sounded.

"It's a cannon!" he thought excitedly. "They're firing a cannon to start the celebration."

Jeff jumped into his clothes and raced downstairs. Then he put his birthday present for Joseph on the table next to Eliza's present.

Since neither Joseph nor Eliza was around, Jeff went outside. There was lots of activity at the rear of the house. "Good morning, Mister Jeff," said Matthew, one of Joseph's servants.

"Good morning, Matthew," said Jeff. "My goodness, I didn't know you would start cooking for the party this soon!"

"Yes, sir," said Matthew. "The fires in the barbecue pits were started long before daybreak. The meat's been on some time already. It will cook very slowly all day long and be just right for the dinner party tonight."

148

When Jeff heard Joseph and Eliza come downstairs, he went back inside. "It's going to be a fine
day, Jeff," said Joseph, looking out the window.

"It's not too cold, either," Jeff said. He knew
that Joseph and Eliza had worried about the
weather.

"No, it isn't," said Joseph. "It's just crisp and
clear. The sun is shining as brightly as anyone
could want it to."

Now Joseph turned from the window and
noticed the presents on the table for the first time.

"Happy Birthday, Joseph!" cried Jeff.

"Happy Birthday, my dear!" said Eliza.

Joseph smiled happily. "I do believe it's the
happiest birthday of my life," he said.

Eliza's present was in a great big package.
It was a fine new suit.

"I'll put it on immediately, my dear, and wear
it all day," said Joseph.

Jeff's present was in a very small package. It

was a pocket knife, the best one he had been able to find.

"It looks like a fine knife, Jeff," said Joseph. He opened the blades and ran his finger over them. "I'll start using it at once. It will see the whole celebration with me. I'll always think of this special occasion whenever I look at it."

Jeff was pleased. He could tell that Joseph really liked both of his presents very much.

After breakfast Joseph said, "It's time to go. We don't want to be late."

"The ceremony can't start without you," said Eliza. She was very proud of her husband.

The carriage came around to the front door. Jeff, Eliza, and Joseph got in and set out for the parade grounds.

There was already a large crowd gathered at the parade grounds when Joseph's carriage arrived.

"I'm glad we don't have to worry about a place

to sit," said Eliza. She knew there were seats reserved for them in the reviewing stand.

The ceremony began. There were speeches by many important people. Then a new flag was raised. It had a brand-new star on it for Mississippi, the twentieth state in the Union.

Many people came up to congratulate Joseph. "We feel you deserve much credit for the admission of Mississippi into the Union," they told him. "It never could have been done without you." Some people knew it was Joseph's birthday, and they congratulated him on that, too.

Then Joseph, Eliza, and Jeff hurried back to their carriage. "I still have many things to do," said Eliza. "The guests will start arriving about four."

"Let's take a drive downtown first," suggested Joseph.

The coachman turned the horses' heads toward town. Soon they were in the heart of Natchez.

"Why, there're flags everywhere!" exclaimed Jeff, and so there were.

The courthouse and stores on the main streets had flags hanging out in front. Many of the stores had signs with "Mississippi, the Twentieth State" or "The Great State of Mississippi" on them. Several of the boys were carrying small flags with the new twentieth star on them.

"Here," said Joseph to the coachman, "stop a minute. Come on, Jeff, let's see whether Mr. Watts has any flags left. He had them especially made for the occasion."

Joseph and Jeff jumped from the carriage and ran into a store. A few minutes later, they were back.

"We have his last one," Jeff told Eliza. Then he stuck his flag upright in the carriage-whip holder. The banner fluttered gaily all the way home.

"There'll be celebrations downtown the rest of

the day," said Joseph. "Since we're having our own celebration, though, I guess we'd better be getting on home."

Jeff, of course, wasn't able to attend the party, but Joseph had said he could sit on the staircase and watch.

There was something interesting to watch right from the beginning, too. When the guests began to arrive, Jeff watched from an upstairs window. Carriage after carriage drove up. The most important gentlemen and ladies of the whole area came. They were dressed in their finest clothes.

Jeff loved to see the horses that pulled the carriages, too. They were all beautiful. Each pair was perfectly matched in size and color.

"I'll move to the staircase now," he thought, when it seemed everyone had arrived. Already both the large dining room and the huge ballroom were aglow with the light from hundreds of candles.

Soon Matthew brought Jeff his supper. The boy ate on the stairs, so he wouldn't miss anything. He had a big plate of barbecued beef with all the side dishes, and second helpings, too.

In the dining room below, Joseph's guests dined on barbecue, too. The big moment of the meal came when all the gentlemen rose and drank a toast. They drank first to the new State of Mississippi. Then they drank to their host Joseph on his birthday.

After supper the ball began. The music and dancing were gay and lively. Everybody laughed and talked. Everyone seemed to be having a wonderful time.

Jeff had thought he'd stay on the stairs until the party was over, but he found his eyes getting heavier and heavier. Several times his head dropped lower and lower until his chin hit his chest, and he woke up with a start.

The sleeping boy was just beginning to dream

of marching with the Mississippi Dragoons when Matthew came to help him up the stairs to his room.

"Well," thought Jeff sleepily, as he climbed into bed, "Joseph promised us a day to remember, and he was right. I'll never forget it." As soon as his head touched the pillow, Jeff was marching off with the Mississippi Dragoons again. He was sound asleep.

Jeff Grows Up

THE FOLLOWING year a new school opened in Woodville. It was called the Academy of Wilkinson County. The teacher who started the school, Mr. Shaw, had come all the way from Boston.

Mr. Davis told Jeff, "Son, your mother and I want to send you to Mr. Shaw's academy."

"That's wonderful!" exclaimed Jeff. "I'd like to go to school close to home."

"Your mother feels exactly the same way," said Mr. Davis. "I must admit that I think it will be very nice, too," he added, as he rubbed his son's blond head.

When Jeff arrived at the academy the first day, he was delighted to find many of his friends from Old Field School there. All of them were glad to see Jeff, too.

"Tell us about your trip to Kentucky," cried one boy.

"Did you see many Indians?" asked another.

"What was the steamboat like?" asked a third.

Jeff liked the academy. It was good to be with his old friends again. He liked the teacher, too. Jeff thought he was a little too strict, but knew he was a good teacher.

Even though Jeff liked the academy, there came a time when he wasn't so sure that he wanted to go to school.

One day Mr. Shaw was assigning homework to his pupils.

"Jeff," said the teacher, "you will memorize the section beginning on page twenty-eight."

Jeff opened his book. It seemed to him that

158

the piece was too long to memorize. In fact, the longer he looked at it, the longer the section seemed.

"Mr. Shaw," Jeff asked at last, "do I have to learn the whole piece?"

"Yes, the whole piece," replied the teacher.

"But, sir," Jeff protested, "don't you think it's awfully long?"

"That's true, Jeff," Mr. Shaw said. "The section is long, and it will be hard to memorize. Still, I have made the assignment."

Usually Jeff didn't say anything about his homework. When his assignments were made, he did them. This time he thought that the assignment was unnecessarily long.

After supper that evening, Jeff spoke to his father and explained that he wanted to quit school for a while. He fully expected his father to object, but much to his surprise Mr. Davis nodded approval.

"All right, son," Mr. Davis began, "if you don't want to go to school, I won't force you to. You will have to go to work, though. No son of mine can be a loafer."

Jeff was overjoyed. He'd rather work than go to school.

"Besides, I need some more help in the cotton fields," Mr. Davis went on. "So, starting tomorrow, you will help out in the fields. I'll have James Pemberton call you in time for work in the morning."

Jeff felt relieved as he climbed into bed that night. "Picking cotton will be easier than going to school," he thought. "Why, I might even have time to fish for a while before supper every night, since I won't have any more homework."

Soon the happy boy was asleep. Even so, he thought he had been asleep for only a few minutes when he felt a hand on his shoulder. It was James Pemberton.

"Mister Jeff," said Jim. "Wake up, Mister Jeff. Your papa said you were going to work in the cotton fields today. Aunt Serena is cooking your breakfast right now."

Jeff sat up. "I feel as though I had just gone to bed," he said, rubbing his eyes, "but I guess I'll have to get up. I don't want to be late going out to the field."

Jim poured water into a bowl. Jeff washed his face and dried it quickly. Then he put on some of his old clothes.

After he had eaten his breakfast, he hurried to the cotton fields. The other workers were picking up their long sacks. They would put the cotton in the sacks as they picked it.

All of the workers greeted Jeff warmly. Then one of them showed him how to pick the cotton. Soon he had started down the long rows with the other workers.

At first, Jeff rather enjoyed picking the fluffy

white balls of cotton. As the morning wore on,
though, the sun grew hotter and hotter. There
was no shade in the field.

Stopping to rest, Jeff saw that he was dropping

far behind the other workers. He started picking cotton as fast as he could, but he couldn't catch up with the other workers.

Jeff was tired long before it was time to quit, but he tried not to slow down. He didn't want anyone to see how tired he really was.

At last it was quitting time. Jeff stood in line with the others to have his sack of cotton weighed. He felt as though his sack weighed a ton, so he was surprised to find that it weighed much less than the sacks of the other workers.

Mr. Davis walked up to see how much Jeff had picked. "Not bad," he said. "Not bad for your first day. In a week, you'll be able to pick twice as much cotton as this."

Jeff's muscles ached. "I don't see how I'll ever be able to pick any more cotton than I did today," he thought.

Then the tired little boy started to walk back to the plantation house.

When he reached home, Jeff bathed and put on clean clothes. A half-hour later he did something he had never done before—he fell asleep at the supper table!

"Jeff! Jeff!" Mamma said, as she gently woke him. "Isaac, please help him up the stairs to his room. I'll be up in a minute."

Jeff fell sound asleep as soon as he reached his bed. Early the next morning he felt a touch on his shoulder.

"Mister Jeff," said a familiar voice. "Mister Jeff. Wake up, Mister Jeff."

Jeff had a hard time opening his eyes, but when he did, he found James Pemberton standing beside his bed.

"Your papa says it's time for you to get up," Jim said. "It's almost time to start picking cotton again."

Jeff dragged himself from his bed. He washed his face and dressed. After breakfast he began to feel better. By the time he reached the cotton fields, he felt full of energy.

The air was still cool early in the day. Soon, however, the sun climbed higher in the sky. Its bright, scorching rays beat on the workers' backs, as they bent to pick the cotton and place it in their sacks.

Jeff worked hard, but he soon became tired. Only a little while after he started, he seemed as tired as he had been at the end of the previous day.

Still, he tried not to let anyone see how tired he was. Gritting his teeth, he worked and worked. He felt as though time had stopped. He couldn't remember whether it was morning or evening. At last, it was time to quit!

"Never in my whole life have I been so glad to have a day come to an end," Jeff thought wearily, as he trudged home.

"I must rest," he said out loud. Then he

stretched out full length under a tree. He lay there for some time. When at last he was ready to start back to the plantation house, he had decided something important.

"It will be hard to tell Papa," he thought, "and it will be even harder to face Mr. Shaw. Still I would rather go back to school than pick cotton."

Jeff picked himself up and walked slowly down the road. "I might go to sleep at the supper table again," he thought, "so I'll talk to Papa as soon as I get home."

Mr. Davis had ridden in from the fields a short time before. Now he was sitting on the long porch, rocking and resting after his day's work.

Jeff walked slowly up the front steps. He stood tall and straight, facing his father.

"Papa," he said, "I've learned my lesson. I'd like to go back to school."

Mr. Davis stopped rocking. "Oh?" he murmured in a questioning tone.

"Yes, sir. I quit school because I thought the teacher's assignment was uncalled for, but I've never worked so hard in my life as I have the last two days. I've decided that, no matter what I do in life, I'll have to work. I think I'd rather work with my head than with my hands."

"A man who has learned to work with his head often finds a laborer's life very hard," Papa remarked.

"I've learned something else, too, Papa," said Jeff. "If I ever own a plantation, I'll never mistreat my workers. They have to work very hard in the fields. I know—I've worked out there with them. I'll never forget how hard it is to pick cotton."

"You have learned an important lesson, son," Mr. Davis said. "If you still feel the same way in the morning, you may return to the academy."

"Yes, sir! Thank you, Papa. You're always so understanding."

Jeff returned to the academy the next day. He never again complained about his schoolwork. In fact, he came to like schoolwork very much. He particularly liked difficult assignments.

By the time Jeff was thirteen years old, he had learned all he could at the county academy. Then his father and his brother Joseph decided to send him to Transylvania University. This school was located in Lexington, Kentucky. It was one of the finest schools in the country.

Jeff studied hard at the university and spent all of his spare time reading. He soon became one of the best students in the school. He also was one of the best speakers.

One day, just before he was to begin his fourth year at Transylvania University, Jeff was appointed to the United States Military Academy at West Point, New York. Many of the finest officers in the army had studied at the Academy. It was an honor to be chosen to go there.

At first Jeff was not sure whether he wanted to be a soldier. "Perhaps I should be a lawyer like my brother Joseph," he thought. "I shall ask his advice. If he thinks I should go to West Point, I shall go and try to make him proud of me."

Joseph urged his youngest brother to accept the commission. So, at the age of sixteen, Jeff went to West Point. He was almost a man.

Soldier, Planter, and Statesman

AT THE United States Military Academy, Cadet Jefferson Davis grew tall and straight. He was strong, handsome, and manly. Although he was younger than many of the other cadets in the school, he was very popular. Everyone admired his good manners and courage.

One day Jeff and his classmates were in the magazine, the building where gun powder and ammunition were stored. The cadets were learning how to make grenades, or fireballs.

Suddenly the fuse of one of the grenades caught fire. The teacher and students were panic-stricken.

"Run for your lives!" shouted the frightened teacher, as he dashed toward the door.

Jeff calmly picked up the dangerous fireball and threw it out a window. His quick thinking and cool courage saved many lives.

Jeff graduated from the Military Academy in 1828 and became a second lieutenant in the United States Army. For seven years he served as an officer on the frontier. Part of the time he served in the Northwest. Part of the time he was stationed in Arkansas, and the rest of the time he served in Indian Territory.

Frequently the young officer was called upon to protect settlers from raiding Indians.

On one scouting trip, Jeff and his small group of soldiers were stopped by a large band of Indians. One warrior stood in the middle of the trail, blocking the way. Jeff asked him for directions. The Indian grunted and pointed.

Jeff suspected that he and his men would ride

into a trap if they followed the Indian's directions, so he made a quick decision.

He dug his spurs into his horse's sides and rode straight toward the Indian. When he reached the warrior, he grabbed him by his scalp lock and dragged him a short distance away. Then he let the Indian drop to the ground.

The brave officer had taken the Indians by surprise. They were so startled by Jeff's quick action and bravery that they allowed him and his troops to ride away unharmed.

Generally, though, Jeff had great respect for Indians. "Most Indians are brave and noble," he said one day to another officer, "but white men have mistreated them many times. Their lands have been taken from them unfairly. They have been forced to move farther west all the time. I cannot stand to see any man mistreated."

Jeff also greatly admired the white settlers who built their homes on the frontier. These

172

sturdy people were exposed constantly to bitter weather and wild animals. At any time they might be attacked by hostile Indians. Yet they braved all of these dangers to carve their farms out of the wilderness.

While serving in the army, Jeff fell in love with Sarah Knox Taylor. Knox, as she was called, was the daughter of a famous army officer, Colonel Zachary Taylor. Jeff and Knox decided to marry, but Jeff was afraid he couldn't support a wife on his low officer's pay. Then he made up his mind to become a cotton planter.

In 1835, Jeff resigned from the army and married Knox. The happy young couple returned to Jeff's beloved Mississippi. Joseph Davis, Jeff's brother, gave them a large tract of land and loaned them money to start their plantation. Jeff and his bride lived with Joseph on his plantation, Hurricane, while Jeff was building his own house.

174

Three months after their marriage, Jeff and Knox became seriously ill with malaria. At first Jeff's condition was worse than Knox's. Then Jeff gradually began to get well, but his wife's health grew worse. Suddenly she died. Jeff was filled with grief.

The heartbroken young planter threw himself into his work. He labored hard to build up his plantation, which he called Brierfield. His old boyhood friend, the faithful James Pemberton helped him.

During these years Jeff read constantly in his spare time. He also took a great interest in the affairs of his state and his country. People began to come to him for advice. Everyone respected his judgment. He was becoming an important man in Mississippi.

Ten years after Knox died, Jeff fell in love with pretty Varina Howell. She fell in love with Jeff, too, and they were married in 1845.

That same year, Jeff was elected to the United States House of Representatives. Leaving Brierfield in the care of faithful James Pemberton, Jeff and Varina went to Washington, D.C. They scarcely had become settled in the nation's capital when war broke out between the United States and Mexico.

The patriotic young congressman felt that he was needed to defend his country. He resigned from Congress and took command of a regiment of Mississippi volunteers.

Colonel Jeff Davis fought valiantly in the war, serving under his old friend and former father-in-law, Zachary Taylor. Jeff and "Old Rough and Ready," as the soldiers called General Taylor, were heroes in the war.

In the Battle of Buena Vista, the Mexican soldiers greatly outnumbered the Americans. During the battle, Jeff was wounded. His foot was shattered, but he wouldn't leave his men.

For eight hours he stayed on his horse and led his soldiers against the enemy.

At last the Mexican army retreated. Only then did Colonel Jeff allow his men to help him from his horse. He was very weak from loss of blood. His wound caused him great pain, but he was happy. The battle had been won.

The people of Mississippi welcomed Colonel Jeff home from the war. He was a great hero. People everywhere talked about his bravery and daring on the battlefield.

"Jeff Davis saved the day for General Taylor," said one man.

"If it hadn't been for Colonel Davis's courage and leadership, the battle would have been lost," echoed another man.

The people of Mississippi were proud of Jeff Davis. Now they honored him by sending him to Congress again. This time he was elected to serve in the United States Senate.

Still on crutches, Jeff walked into the Senate in 1847 to join many great men who were gathered there. Of all the brilliant thinkers and speakers in the Senate, Jeff most admired John C. Calhoun of South Carolina.

Senator Calhoun twice had been Vice-President of the United States and had served in the Senate for many years. Although he was now sixty-five years old, Senator Calhoun was still a man of principle and dignity. He was the most outstanding leader from the southern states.

In 1851, Jeff resigned from the Senate to run for the office of Governor of Mississippi. Although he was defeated in this election, his talents were not wasted for long.

Franklin Pierce, an old friend of Jeff's, became President in 1853. He asked Jeff to serve in his cabinet as Secretary of War.

"There is no one in the country who knows the needs of the army as well as you, Jeff," Mr. Pierce said. "You were trained to be a soldier at West Point. You have served your country well as an officer and as a congressman. Jeff, I need you. The country needs you."

Jeff couldn't refuse this plea. Although he wanted to stay on his plantation, he felt a call to duty. He accepted the job.

For four years, Secretary Davis devoted his

great energy and ability to improving the United States Army. He tried to bring it up to date.

Jeff always hated war, but he felt that the country should be prepared in case there should be another war with a foreign country.

He saw to it that the pay of soldiers and officers was raised. He provided the soldiers with the latest weapons and trained the troops in the newest methods of warfare.

While he was Secretary of War, he bought camels for the army. At first many people thought that he was foolish, but they soon discovered that camels were far better than horses in the desert regions of the country.

Camels could travel faster and farther than horses in desert lands. They could go for a long time without water, and they could carry much heavier loads than horses could carry. These awkward animals were used by the soldiers in the dry Southwest for several years.

Jeff was greatly interested in railroads, too. He believed that some day people would be able to travel from coast to coast on trains. He even sent out soldiers to map the best routes for railroads to cross the country.

By the time his term of office as Secretary of War was over, Jeff Davis had improved the army greatly. Now he hoped to return to Brierfield and the life of a cotton planter.

Again, the people of Mississippi called him to duty. They wanted him to represent them again in the United States Senate.

Many of the older leaders were gone now. John C. Calhoun was dead. Jeff took his place as the leading senator from the South. He was a fine speaker. His clear words and beautiful voice caused even many of his enemies to listen to him. He had many friends and many followers. Jefferson Davis was recognized everywhere as an outstanding statesman.

President of the Confederacy

ONE DAY in 1860, a small group of southern senators gathered in a room in the capital. The men were greatly excited. Many of them were very angry.

"Gentlemen," one man said, "the federal government has not respected our rights."

"That is true," said another man. "We have been treated unfairly. The laws tend to favor the northern states. There is only one thing for us to do." He pounded the table with his fist. "We must leave the Union!"

"Let us not be rash, gentlemen," warned a tall, handsome man. This man was Jefferson Davis.

"We should try to understand the North's point of view," Senator Davis said. "At the same time, we should try to make the northerners understand our position. After all, there are always two sides to every argument."

"It is easy to say that, Senator," replied the first man, "but it is hard to endure these wrongs. The time has come for action."

A third senator spoke up. "Many years ago, the American colonists felt they were being mistreated by the government of Great Britain. The colonists withdrew from the British Empire and formed the United States of America.

"Today, we people in the South feel that we are being abused also. We feel that we have a right to leave the Union and to establish our own government."

"I agree with you, sir," Senator Davis said kindly. "I must warn you, though, that many people in the North do not recognize the right of secession. May I remind you also that the American colonies were forced to fight for their independence."

The senators nodded their heads. Then Senator Davis went on.

"If the southern states secede, the federal government may try to force them to stay in the Union. If that happens, it will mean war."

"Then we shall have to defend ourselves," the second man said boldly.

"What will you do, Senator Davis, if your state secedes from the Union?" the first man asked.

"Sir, I am a citizen of the United States. I have loved my country very much. I have fought for her. Still, I am a citizen of Mississippi first. If my state leaves the Union, I have no choice but to resign from the Senate and go with my state. If war comes, I will fight to defend my state."

"Bravo! Bravo!" shouted the other senators together. "Hurrah for Jefferson Davis!"

Jefferson Davis raised his hand. The room was very quiet.

"Gentlemen," Jeff said sadly, "let us make every effort to preserve the Union. If our efforts fail, then we'll have to secede. If this happens, let us hope the federal government will allow us to go in peace."

Unfortunately, the argument between the North and the South became more bitter as time went on. Finally, in December, 1860, South Carolina withdrew from the Union. Quickly, other southern states seceded also.

When Mississippi seceded, Jeff Davis was heartsick, but he knew he must follow his beloved state. So he resigned from the Senate and returned to Brierfield.

After the southern states left the Union, they banded together for protection. Meeting in Montgomery, Alabama, leaders from the seceded states drew up a constitution. They formed the

Confederate States of America—or the Confederacy, as it was called.

The new Confederacy needed a leader. It needed a man who had intelligence, honesty, and courage. It needed a man who was both understanding and patient. It needed a man who loved the South. It needed a man who was respected by all the people of the South.

Only one person seemed to meet all of these needs. That man was Jefferson Davis. On February 18, 1861, the handsome former senator became President of the Confederacy.

Meanwhile, the federal government was determined that the southern states should not secede. The government tried to force them to stay in the Union. War broke out!

President Jefferson Davis met with his advisers to plan what they would do.

"Gentlemen," the President began, "my worst fears have been realized. We must fight to de-

fend our beliefs. We must fight to defend our states. I fear that we are at a great disadvantage——"

One of the President's cabinet members interrupted. "We have many things in our favor, sir. We have gallant and able generals—men such as Robert E. Lee, Albert Sidney Johnston, and Leonidas Polk."

"I know," the President said. "I knew these men at West Point, and I served with them in the army. They are good soldiers. The men under them will fight bravely, but you must remember that we are greatly outnumbered by the soldiers of the North."

"If the Union wishes to force its laws on us," said another adviser, "its soldiers must come South to do it. Then we shall have them. Our soldiers know the land well. We should have an easy victory."

"Do not be mistaken, my friends," the President warned. "We have able generals and brave soldiers, but how shall we arm them? How shall we feed them? How shall we clothe them? We have few factories in the South to make the things we need. We have few railroads to move our men and supplies from one place to another. We have practically no navy.

"No, gentlemen! Victory will not be easy. This war may be long and bloody. The Union may have many advantages over us, but we shall not give up without a fight."

The war was long and bloody. The country was torn apart by bitter fighting. For four long years, Confederate soldiers fought Union soldiers. Gradually, one by one, the Confederate generals were forced to surrender.

Finally, in 1865, the war was over. The Confederacy was defeated. Then the nation was united once again.

Once the fighting was over, Jefferson Davis,

the great man from Mississippi, refused to hold any grudges against the North. He refused to harbor feelings of hatred and ill will against his northern neighbors. He accepted his defeat nobly, as a true gentleman.

One lovely spring day in 1886, a large crowd gathered at Fair View, Kentucky. A small church was being dedicated there.

The guest of honor for this occasion sat quietly at ease on the speakers' stand. Though his cheeks were hollow and his face had many deep lines, he was still handsome.

Another man rose. He was going to introduce the guest of honor. He moved to the front of the platform. The crowd grew quiet.

"Dear friends," the speaker began, "our guest of honor today is here for a very special reason. The church that is being dedicated today was built on the very spot where he was born.

"Even before our guest was born on June 3,

1808, the house that stood on this ground was famous. It was the first house in this area that had glass windows. People came from miles around to see the wonder of glass windows.

"Little did those curious people know that the house would become famous as the birthplace of a great man.

"Our guest of honor is well known to all of you as a man of outstanding character and ability. He is remembered as a gallant soldier, a brilliant statesman, a noble gentleman. He is best known, however, as the former President of the Confederate States of America.

"Ladies and gentlemen, it is a great privilege for me to present to you a man whose love for the South and service to the South will never be forgotten. I present to you a man whose name will go down in history as a symbol of the South. I present to you our distinguished guest of honor, Mr. Jefferson Davis."

DO YOU REMEMBER?

1. When and where was Jeff Davis born?
2. What was the name of the Davis plantation in Mississippi?
3. Why did Jeff try to find dogwood blossoms?
4. Why did Jeff and James Pemberton brush Riptide's coat a hundred strokes a day?
5. What happened to Jeff and Pollie when Jeff said, "We will not run"?
6. What Indians lived in northern Mississippi?
7. How far was it from the Davis plantation in Mississippi to Kentucky?
8. Why did Jeff's mother and father send him to Kentucky with Major Hinds?
9. Why did keelboatmen have to walk home after floating goods down the river?
10. What was the name of General Andrew Jackson's plantation in Tennessee?
11. Why were people so excited about seeing a steamboat on the river?
12. What two things did Captain Robinson DeHart always carry with him?

13. How did Jefferson Davis show great courage at West Point Military Academy?

14. Which member of the United States Senate did he admire most and why?

15. Why did he purchase camels for the United States Army when he was Secretary of War?

16. What important position did he hold in the South during the War between the States?

IMPORTANT THINGS TO LOOK UP

1. What is the "Cotton Belt," and across what states does it extend?

2. Who were the following persons mentioned in the story: John C. Calhoun, Andrew Jackson, Albert Sidney Johnston, Robert E. Lee, Franklin Pierce, Leonidas Polk, Zachary Taylor?

3. Why did the United States go to war with Mexico in 1846, and where were most of the important battles fought during the war?

4. Which states seceded from the Union and joined the Confederate States of America?

5. What was the first steamboat used on the Ohio and Mississippi rivers?

194

INTERESTING THINGS TO DO

1. Read about Jefferson Davis in an encyclopedia and make a list of things that he did to show that he was a great American. Then write a story about him and read it to the class.

2. Draw a map showing what the United States was like just before the War between the States. Color blue the states that fought with the North during the War and color gray the states that fought with the Confederacy during the War.

3. Find out how steamboats changed the methods of transportation and travel in the country during Jefferson Davis' life.

4. Make a report about Jefferson Davis' bringing camels to America for the Army to use.

OTHER BOOKS TO READ

Abraham Lincoln, Ingri and Edgar D'Aulaire. Doubleday.

Andrew Jackson, Frontier Statesman, Clara Ingram Judson. Follett.

Billy Yank and Johnny Reb: How They Fought and Made Up, Earl Schenck Miers. Rand McNally.

Brother against Brother, Stories of the War between the States, Phyllis Fenner. Morrow.

Robert E. Lee and the Road of Honor, Hodding Carter. Trade Edition, Random House. School Edition, Hale.

Robert Fulton and the Steamboat, Ralph Nading Hill. Trade Edition, Random House. School Edition, Hale.

Zack Taylor: Young Rough and Ready, Katharine E. Wilkie. Trade and School Editions, Bobbs-Merrill.

WHEN JEFF DAVIS LIVED

1808   JEFF DAVIS WAS BORN IN KENTUCKY, JUNE 3.

There were 17 states in the Union.

The population of the country was about 6,800,000.

Thomas Jefferson was President.

1809–   JEFF GREW UP IN MISSISSIPPI AND WENT TO
1823   SCHOOL IN KENTUCKY.

Abraham Lincoln was born, 1809.

The War of 1812 was fought, 1812–1815.

1824–   JEFF WENT TO THE U.S. MILITARY ACADEMY.
1828   The Erie Canal was completed, 1825.

John Quincy Adams was President, 1825–1829.

1829– 1852	JEFF WAS A SOLDIER, PLANTER, AND CONGRESS-MAN.
	Peter Cooper built the first steam locomotive in the United States, 1830.
	The Mexican War was fought, 1846–1848.
	Harriet Beecher Stowe's *Uncle Tom's Cabin* was published, 1852.
1853– 1860	JEFF WAS SECRETARY OF WAR AND SENATOR FROM MISSISSIPPI.
	Franklin Pierce was President, 1853–1857.
	Stephen Foster's "Old Black Joe" was published, 1860.
	Eleven southern states formed the Confederate States of America, 1860–1861.
1861– 1865	DAVIS WAS PRESIDENT OF THE CONFEDERACY.
	The War between the States was fought, 1861–1865.
	The Emancipation Proclamation was issued, 1863.
1866– 1867	DAVIS WAS HELD PRISONER IN FORTRESS MONROE.
	The first transatlantic cable was laid, 1866.
	The United States purchased Alaska, 1867.

197

1868–	DAVIS LIVED IN RETIREMENT.

1868–
1888 DAVIS LIVED IN RETIREMENT.

The first transcontinental railroad was completed, 1869.

Alexander G. Bell invented the telephone, 1876.

Thomas Edison invented the phonograph, 1878, and the electric light bulb, 1879.

1889 JEFF DAVIS DIED, DECEMBER 6.

There were 42 states in the Union.

The population of the country was about 62,500,000.

Benjamin Harrison was President.

HELP WITH WORDS

cabinet (kăb′ĭ nĕt) : group of advisers whom the President of the United States chooses to help him run different departments of the government

cadet (kȧ dĕt′) : person taking military training

cardinal bird (kär′dĭ năl) : brightly colored songbird, sometimes called a redbird because the male has bright red feathers and a red bill

Choctaw (chŏk′tô) : Indian tribe which formerly lived in Mississippi but now lives in Oklahoma

198

constitution (kŏn′stĭ tū′shŭn) : written statement of the laws and beliefs of a state or nation, used to guide the government

currycomb (kûr′ĭ kōm′) : kind of comb with metal teeth used to brush a horse

dedicated (dĕd′ĭ kāt′ĕd) : devoted to some worthy person or cause

distinguished (dĭs tĭng′gwĭsht) : noted, famous

dragoon (drȧ gōon′) : heavily armed mounted soldier

frisk: scamper about happily, frolic

gallant (găl′ănt) : brave and noble

gangplank (găng′plăngk′) : long movable walk or bridge used for boarding or leaving a ship

grenade (grė̇ nād′) : small bomb or shell filled with high explosives

harbor (här′bēr) : hold on to a grudge against someone or something

intelligence (ĭn tĕl′ĭ jĕns) : ability to think, reason, or understand

magnolia tree (măg nō′lĭ ȧ) : tree with waxy leaves and large beautiful flowers found in the South

malaria (mȧ lâr′ĭ ȧ) : disease caused by the bite of a certain kind of mosquito

Natchez (năch′ĕz) : city in Mississippi, located on the Mississippi River

politics (pŏl′ĭ tĭks) : beliefs held by a group of people about running the government

preparation (prĕp′à rā′shŭn) : work of getting something ready

procession (prò sĕsh′ŭn) : group of people moving in an orderly line, as in a parade

project (prŏj′ĕkt) : piece of work

punkah (pŭng′kà) : large overhead fan moved back and forth by means of a rope

secession (sè sĕsh′ŭn) : act of withdrawing from an organization or a country

sounding: process of measuring the depth of water in a river, lake, or ocean by letting down a weighted line

spinet (spĭn′ĕt) : old-time musical instrument, something like a piano

symbol (sĭm′bŭl) : sign or emblem; something that stands for something else, as a drawing, letters or numbers

trace: path, trail, road

weigh anchor: lift or hoist anchor from the water

wharf (hwôrf) : pier or dock where boats may be loaded and unloaded

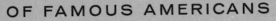

Childhood

OF FAMOUS AMERICANS

CHILDHOOD
OF FAMOUS
AMERICANS

COLONIAL DAYS

JAMES OGLETHORPE, *Parks*
MYLES STANDISH, *Stevenson*
PETER STUYVESANT, *Widdemer*
POCAHONTAS, *Seymour*
VIRGINIA DARE, *Stevenson*
WILLIAM BRADFORD, *Smith*
WILLIAM PENN, *Mason*

STRUGGLE for INDEPENDENCE

ANTHONY WAYNE, *Stevenson*
BEN FRANKLIN, *Stevenson*
BETSY ROSS, *Weil*
DAN MORGAN, *Bryant*
ETHAN ALLEN, *Winders*
FRANCIS MARION, *Steele*
GEORGE ROGERS CLARK, *Wilkie*
GEORGE WASHINGTON, *Stevenson*
ISRAEL PUTNAM, *Stevenson*
JOHN PAUL JONES, *Snow*
JOHN SEVIER, *Steele*
MARTHA WASHINGTON, *Wagoner*
MOLLY PITCHER, *Stevenson*

NATHAN HALE, *Stevenson*
NATHANAEL GREENE, *Peckham*
PAUL REVERE, *Stevenson*
TOM JEFFERSON, *Monsell*

EARLY NATIONAL GROWTH

ABIGAIL ADAMS, *Wagoner*
ALEC HAMILTON, *Higgins*
ANDY JACKSON, *Stevenson*
DAN WEBSTER, *Smith*
DOLLY MADISON, *Monsell*
ELI WHITNEY, *Snow*
HENRY CLAY, *Monsell*
JAMES FENIMORE COOPER, *Winders*
JAMES MONROE, *Widdemer*
JOHN AUDUBON, *Mason*
JOHN MARSHALL, *Monsell*
JOHN QUINCY ADAMS, *Weil*
LUCRETIA MOTT, *Burnett*
MATTHEW CALBRAITH PERRY, *Scharbach*
NANCY HANKS, *Stevenson*
OLIVER HAZARD PERRY, *Long*
RACHEL JACKSON, *Govan*
ROBERT FULTON, *Henry*
SAMUEL MORSE, *Snow*
STEPHEN DECATUR, *Smith*
STEPHEN FOSTER, *Higgins*
WASHINGTON IRVING, *Widdemer*
ZACK TAYLOR, *Wilkie*